LOCOMOTIVES

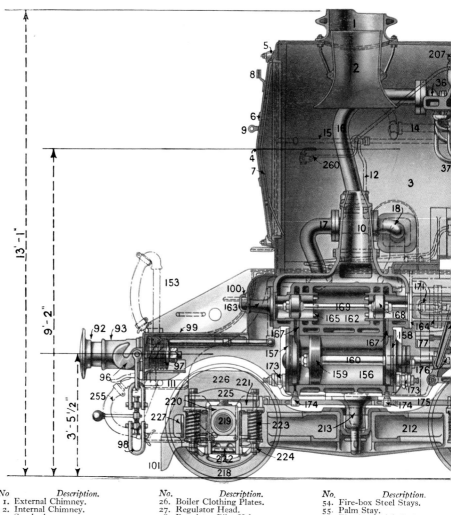

No	Description.	No.	Description.	No.	Description.
1.	External Chimney.	26.	Boiler Clothing Plates.	54.	Fire-box Steel Stays.
2.	Internal Chimney.	27.	Regulator Head.	55.	Palm Stay.
3.	Smoke-box.	28.	Regulator Pilot Valve.	56.	Fire-box Brick Arch.
4.	Smoke-box Door.	29.	Regulator Main Valve.	57.	Fire-hole Deflector Plate.
5.	Smoke-box Door Fastenings.	30.	Regulator Connecting Link.	58.	Fire-bars.
6.	Smoke-box Door Hinges.	31.	Regulator Rod.	59.	Fire-bar Bearers.
7.	Smoke-box Door Liner Plate.	32	Regulator Stuffing-box.	60.	Fire-bar Bearer Bracket.
8.	Lamp Irons.	33.	Regulator Handle.	61.	Fire-box Washout Doors.
9.	Front Handrail.	34.	Gusset Stay for Fire-box Back-plate.	62.	Washout Plugs.
10.	Blast-pipe.	35.	Main Steam-pipe in Boilers.	63.	Safety Valves.
11.	Blast-pipe Cap.	36.	Superheater Header.	64	Safety Valve Seating.
12.	Blower Pipe.	37.	Superheater Elements.	65.	Whistle.
13.	Gusset Stay for Smoke-box Tube-plate.	38.	Superheater Flue-tubes.	66.	Whistle Handle.
		39.	Boiler Tubes.	67.	Fusible Plugs.
14.	Vacuum-brake Ejector Exhaust Pipe.	40.	Smoke-box Tube-plate.	68.	Expansion Handle.
15.	Handrails.	41.	Fire-box Throat-plate.	69.	Fire-box Steadying Plate.
16.	Steam-pipe in Smoke-box to Cylinders.	42.	Fire-box Wrapper-plate.	70.	Fire-hole Door.
		43.	Fire-box Door-plate.	71.	Fire-hole Ring Shield.
17	Steam-pipe to Inside Cylinders.	44.	Inner Fire-box Door-plate.	72.	Boiler Pressure Gauge.
18.	Steam-pipe to Outside Cylinders.	45.	Fire-box Tube-plate.	73.	Boiler Water Gauge and Pro
19.	Boiler Barrel, First Ring.	46.	Inner Fire-box Wrapper-plate.	74.	Dry Steam-pipe to Steam-coc
20.	Boiler Barrel, Second Ring.	47.	Fire-box Crown.	75.	Delivery Pipe from Injector.
21.	Boiler Barrel, First Ring Longi-tudinal Joint.	48.	Foundation Ring.	76.	Clack Box.
		49.	Fire-hole Ring.	77.	Vacuum-brake Ejector.
22.	Dome.	50.	Fire-box Longitudinal Stays.	78.	Driver's Operating Valve Ha Vacuum-brake.
23.	Dome Strengthening Plate.	51.	Fire-box Transverse Stays.		
24.	Dome Cover.	52.	Fire-box Crown Vertical Stays.	79.	Oil-box for Main Bearing of (Wheels.
25.	Dome Casing.	53.	Fire-box Copper Stays.		

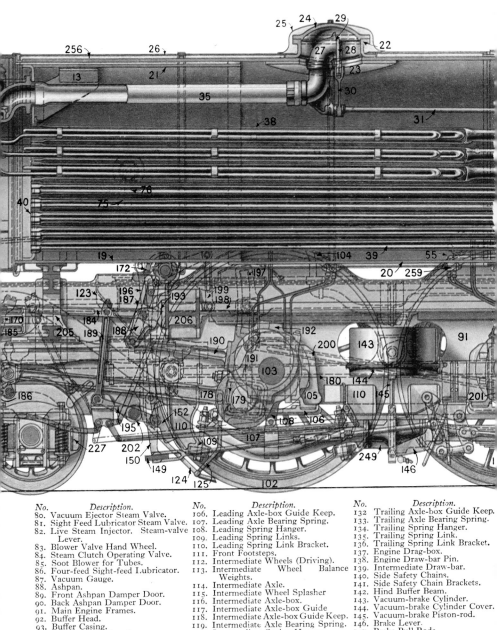

No.	Description.	No.	Description.	No.	Description.
80.	Vacuum Ejector Steam Valve.	106.	Leading Axle-box Guide Keep.	132	Trailing Axle-box Guide Keep.
81.	Sight Feed Lubricator Steam Valve.	107.	Leading Axle Bearing Spring.	133.	Trailing Axle Bearing Spring.
82.	Live Steam Injector. Steam-valve Lever.	108.	Leading Spring Hanger.	134.	Trailing Spring Hanger.
		109.	Leading Spring Links.	135.	Trailing Spring Link.
83.	Blower Valve Hand Wheel.	110.	Leading Spring Link Bracket.	136.	Trailing Spring Link Bracket.
84.	Steam Clutch Operating Valve.	111.	Front Footsteps.	137.	Engine Drag-box.
85.	Soot Blower for Tubes.	112.	Intermediate Wheels (Driving).	138.	Engine Draw-bar Pin.
86.	Four-feed Sight-feed Lubricator.	113.	Intermediate Wheel Balance Weights.	139.	Intermediate Draw-bar.
87.	Vacuum Gauge.			140.	Side Safety Chains.
88.	Ashpan.	114.	Intermediate Axle.	141.	Side Safety Chain Brackets.
89.	Front Ashpan Damper Door.	115.	Intermediate Wheel Splasher	142.	Hind Buffer Beam.
90.	Back Ashpan Damper Door.	116.	Intermediate Axle-box.	143.	Vacuum-brake Cylinder.
91.	Main Engine Frames.	117.	Intermediate Axle-box Guide	144.	Vacuum-brake Cylinder Cover.
92.	Buffer Head.	118.	Intermediate Axle-box Guide Keep.	145.	Vacuum-brake Piston-rod.
93.	Buffer Casing.	119.	Intermediate Axle Bearing Spring.	146.	Brake Lever.
94.	Buffer Beam (Front).	120.	Intermediate Spring Hanger.	147.	Brake Pull Rods.
95.	Buffer Beam Stay.	121.	Intermediate Spring Link Brackets.	148.	Brake Adjusting Nuts.
96.	Drawbar and Hook.	122.	Frame Stay.	149.	Brake Crossbeam.
97.	Draw Spring.	123.	Outside Cylinder Slide-bar Bracket and Sand-box	150.	Brake Hanger.
ector.	98. Screw Coupling.			151.	Brake Hanger Bracket.
Stand.	99. Front Platform Plate.	124.	Sand-pipe.	152.	Brake-block.
	100. Steam-chest Cover Plate and Handle.	125.	Sand-pipe Stay.	153.	Vacuum-brake Train-pipe.
		126.	Sand-box Lids.	154.	Vacuum Pump.
		127.	Side Platform Plate.	155.	Outside Cylinder.
	101. Life Guards.	128.	Trailing Wheel.	156.	Inside Cylinder.
dle for	102. Leading Wheels (Driving).	129.	Trailing Axle.	157.	Cylinder Front Cover.
	103. Crank-axle.	130.	Trailing Axle-box.	158.	Cylinder Rear Cover.
oupled	104. Leading Wheel Splasher.	131.	Trailing Axle-box Guide.	159.	Piston.
	105. **Leading Axle-box Guide.**				

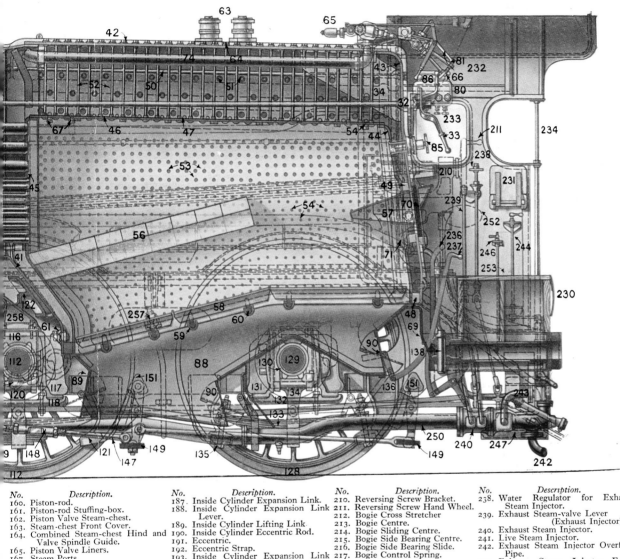

No.	Description.	No.	Description.	No.	Description.	No.	Description.
160.	Piston-rod.	187.	Inside Cylinder Expansion Link.	210.	Reversing Screw Bracket.	238.	Water Regulator for Exhaust Steam Injector.
161.	Piston-rod Stuffing-box.	188.	Inside Cylinder Expansion Link Lever.	211.	Reversing Screw Hand Wheel.	239.	Exhaust Steam-valve Lever (Exhaust Injector).
162.	Piston Valve Steam-chest.			212.	Bogie Cross Stretcher		
163.	Steam-chest Front Cover.	189.	Inside Cylinder Lifting Link.	213.	Bogie Centre.	240.	Exhaust Steam Injector.
164.	Combined Steam-chest Hind and Valve Spindle Guide.	190.	Inside Cylinder Eccentric Rod.	214.	Bogie Sliding Centre.	241.	Live Steam Injector.
		191.	Eccentric.	215.	Bogie Side Bearing Centre.	242.	Exhaust Steam Injector Overflow Pipe.
165.	Piston Valve Liners.	192.	Eccentric Strap.	216.	Bogie Side Bearing Slide.		
167.	Steam Ports.	193.	Inside Cylinder Expansion Link Bracket.	217.	Bogie Control Spring.	243.	Exhaust Steam Injector Feed-water Pipe.
168.	Piston Valve Head.			218.	Bogie Wheel.		
169.	Piston Valve Spindle.	194.	Reversing Shaft	219.	Bogie Axle.	244.	Feed-water Cock Spindle.
170.	Piston Valve Crosshead.	195.	Inside Cylinder Reversing Shaft.	220.	Bogie Axle-box.	245.	Feed-water Cock.
171.	Piston Valve Spindle Gland.	196.	Connecting Link between Reversing Shafts.	221.	Bogie Axle-box Guide.	246.	Coal Watering Cock.
172.	Reversing Shaft Clutch.			222.	Bogie Axle-box Guide Keep.	247.	Rear Footsteps.
173.	Water Release Valves.	197.	Outside Cylinder Expansion Link.	223.	Bogie Bearing-spring.	248.	Vacuum Train-pipe Drip Trap.
174.	Cylinder Drain-cock.	198.	Outside Cylinder Radius Rod.	224.	Bogie Bearing-spring Link.	249.	Grease Separator for Exhaust Steam
175.	Cylinder Drain-cock Rod.	199.	Outside Cylinder Lifting Link.	225.	Bogie Bearing-spring Beam.	250.	Exhaust Steam-pipe.
176.	Inside Piston-rod Crosshead.	200.	Outside Cylinder Eccentric Rod.	226	Bogie Frame Plate.	251.	Name Plate.
177.	Inside Slide-bars.	201.	Eccentric Crank.	227.	Bogie Frame Stay.	252.	Number Plate.
178.	Inside Connecting Rod.	202	Inside Cylinder Reversing Shaft Brackets.	228.	Bogie Wheel Splasher.	253.	Wood Platform.
179.	Inside Connecting Rod—Big-end.			229.	Fire Screen.	254	Cover for Outside Cylinder Expansion Link.
180.	Outside Connecting Rod.	203.	Outside Cylinder Crosshead.	230.	Fall Plate.		
181.	Coupling Rods.	204.	Outside Cylinder Slide-bars.	231.	Engineman's Seat.	255.	Steam-pipe for Carriage Heating.
182.	Coupling Rod Crankpin.	205.	Inside Slide-bar Bracket and Frame Stay.	232.	Cab.	256.	Magnesia Covering.
183.	Reversing Shaft Balance Spring.			233.	Cab Side Windows	257.	Blow-off Cock.
184.	Inside Cylinder Radius Rod.	206.	Frame Stay.	234.	Cab Handrail.	258.	Oil-pipes to Main Axle Bearing.
185.	Inside Cylinder Combination Lever.	207.	Vacuum Relief Valves.	235.	Cab Front Window.	259.	Oil-box for Axle-box Guides.
186.	Inside Cylinder Connecting Link to Crosshead.	208.	Reversing Shaft Brackets.	236.	Sanding-cocks Lever.	260.	Steam-cock for Tube Cleaner.
		209.	Reversing Rod.	237	Ashpan Damper Lever.		

LOCOMOTIVES

THEIR CONSTRUCTION, MAINTENANCE AND OPERATION

WITH NOTES ON ELECTRIC, INTERNAL COMBUS-
TION AND OTHER FORMS OF MOTIVE POWER

By

A. MORTON BELL, O.B.E.

M.I.Mech.E., M.I.Loco.E.

With Foreword by A. C. CARR, V.D., M.I.Mech.E., M.I.E.(India)

President Institution of Locomotive Engineers, 1935–36

Second Edition, 1935

VOLUME I

LONDON

VIRTUE & COMPANY LIMITED

19–21 THAVIES INN, HOLBORN CIRCUS, E.C.1

PRINTED IN GREAT BRITAIN BY THE EDINBURGH PRESS, EDINBURGH AND LONDON

FOREWORD

THE writer of these volumes has produced in a remarkably concise manner a work on recent developments and modern practice in connection with steam and other locomotives which should prove a useful addition to the literature available on the subject.

He has used the practical experience gained over a period of fifty years, in design, manufacture, and operation of steam locomotives, in compiling the notes and information given.

A work of this description must be of great value to all railway locomotive staffs in any country, and indeed to all railway men and the general public who may be interested in the steam locomotive and its competitors.

A. C. CARR, V.D., M.I.MECH.E., M.I.E.(INDIA).

President Institution of Locomotive Engineers, 1935–36.

INTRODUCTION

IN the following pages the writer presents in a comprehensive form a general survey of the more important aspects of the construction, operation and maintenance of locomotives—steam, Diesel, electric, internal combustion, fireless, etc. Whilst historical matter has been more or less avoided, the development of locomotives from the somewhat elementary construction of fifty years ago is often referred to, so that the more refined details embodied in the machines of to-day can be more readily understood.

Locomotive design and construction will bear any amount of study and research, and in regard to many of the details it may truly be said that there are few which have not undergone considerable successive improvements before reaching the form in which we find them to-day. In operation and maintenance the progress has been remarkable during late years; perhaps the example of the mass-produced motor car has had its effect on this problem in railway operation. Now repairs are carried out to a well-defined programme which ensures attention to every detail. The " belt " system, adopted in many of the large repair shops, coincides very closely with the procedure accepted for many of the modern mechanical industries. To make this possible, the standardization of parts has been a necessary operation, and where one railway could boast of, say, a dozen types of locomotives, to-day three or four are made to suffice; even in these many of the important details are interchangeable.

The lay-out and furnishing of shops and sheds will prove interesting to many readers connected with the operation. The ever-increasing competition of the internal combustion engine and its close associate, electrical traction, is referred to, and attention given to the rapid developments experienced during the past few years.

Much of the material has been taken from the experience of practical men as recorded in articles which have appeared in *The Locomotive* and its affiliated publications, and finally the thanks of both Author and Publisher are due to those Firms who have provided photographs, drawings or blocks necessary to illustrate their various products.

CONTENTS

Chapter I

GENERAL DESCRIPTION

Chapter II

THE BOILER

Chapter III

SUPERHEATING

Chapter IV

CYLINDERS AND VALVES

Chapter V

FRAMING AND WHEELS

CONTENTS

Chapter VI

LUBRICATION

Chapter VII

TENDERS

Chapter VIII

CONTINUOUS BRAKES

Chapter IX

FEED-WATER

LIST OF COLOURED ILLUSTRATIONS AND FOLDING PLATES

CHAPTER I

General Description of Standard Types—Wheel arrangements—Track Gauges—Disposition of Cylinders—Tractive Effort—Conditions of Service—Train Resistance—Weight Distribution, etc.

General.

A STEAM locomotive may be said to comprise four principal parts:

1. The boiler, in which steam is generated by combustion of fuel in its contained furnace, or fire-box, thereby providing the power.

2. The engine, comprising the cylinders, motion, etc., from whence the energy of the steam can be converted into tractive effort at the rails.

3. The frame, or " chassis," on which the boiler and engine are carried, and by which the power is transmitted to the draw-gear and the connected train.

4. The tender, the accompanying vehicle, on which the fuel and water required for the boiler are carried. In the case of tank engines, the supplies are contained in the receptacles arranged on the frame of the locomotive itself.

Wheel Arrangements.

The different wheel arrangements met with are, naturally, numerous and diverse, to meet the variety of services locomotives are required to perform. Engines used to be classified under two main headings, " passenger " and " goods," but these no longer obtain, those of the former having but one pair of driving wheels, or " singles," as they are termed, being now but items of history. Engines with four, six, or eight driving wheels coupled are necessary to obtain the required adhesion for main line passenger traffic, whilst for goods and mineral trains, those having six, eight, or ten drivers coupled are types in general use. Locomotives having the unusual arrangement of twelve and fourteen wheels coupled are in service abroad for mineral traffic, but ten driving wheels coupled are, so far, the maxima for adhesion in this country. The wheel arrangements quoted in the adjoining table are nearly all to be found under both tender and tank locomotives; the latter carrying their supplies of fuel and water in bunkers and tanks on the framing of the engine, as already mentioned.

Engines used for either passenger or goods trains are known as "mixed" traffic locomotives.

Some of the chief wheel arrangements of modern locomotives:

Leading End of Engine to Left.

British and American Notation.		French Symbol.*	German Symbol.*
2–2–2†	o O o	1–1–1	1. A. 1.
4–2–2†	o o O o	2–1–1	2. A. 1.
2–4–2	o O O o	1–2–1	1. B. 1.
4–4–0	o o O O	2–2–0	2. B.
4–4–2	o o O O o	2–2–1	2. B. 1.
0–6–0	O O O	0–3–0	C.
2–6–0	o O O O	1–3–0	1. C.
4–6–0	o o O O O	2–3–0	2. C.
4–6–2	o o O O O o	2–3–1	2. C. 1.
0–6–4	O O O o o	0–3–2	C. 2.
0–8–0	O O O O	0–4–0	D.
2–8–0	o O O O O	1–4–0	1. D.
0–10–0	O O O O O	0–5–0	E.
2–10–0	o O O O O O	1–5–0	1. E.

Many other wheel arrangements are in use, but these can be readily symbolized from the foregoing table.

The particular information required when considering the most satisfactory dimensions, type and design of locomotives for any special service may be summarized as: Gauge of railway—that is, distance between rails, particular traffic to be worked or hauled, extreme load.

Track Gauges of the World.

Normal and Standard	Great Britain, Continent of Europe ‡ (excluding Spain, Portugal and Russia), U.S.A., Canada, Mexico, Egypt, Palestine, Turkey, Persia, Commonwealth of Australia, N.S.W., etc.	4 ft. 8½ in.
Broad	India, Argentine, Chili, Portugal and Spain	5 ft. 6 in.
	Ireland, Brazil, South Australia, Victoria, etc.	5 ft. 3 in.
	Russia	5 ft.

* In the French and German symbols the driving and carrying axles are quoted, and not the number of driving wheels, thus a 2–4–2 in the British or American notation become 1–2–1 in the French, and 1. B. 1. in the German, the capital letters being used for the drivers.

† Practically obsolete.

‡ The French gauge is 1,500 mm., measured between centres of rails.

Metre   India, Central Africa, F.M.S., Siam, French China.   3 ft. 3⅜ in.

Narrow   South Africa (Cape railways), Japan, Queensland,
                 Tasmania, etc.   .   .   .   .   .   .   3 ft. 6 in.

             Isle of Man   .   .   .   .   3 ft.

             India, West Africa, Gold Coast, Sierra Leone, South
                 America   .   .   .   .   2 ft. 6 in.

Limits (see diagram of British Standard Gauges, Fig. 1), grade and curves, type and weight of permanent way, strength of bridges, climatic

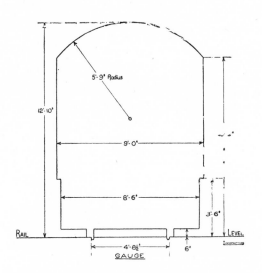

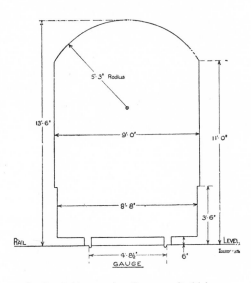

England (Average). Gauge, 4 ft. 8½ ins.   Scotland (Average). Gauge, 4 ft. 8½ ins.

FIG. 1.

conditions; and, further, any legal restrictions must be borne in mind, as these may have an important effect on design.

The power developed by a locomotive must primarily depend on the steam generation in the boiler and the tractive effort, as determined by the diameter and stroke of the cylinders, diameter of the driving wheels, and working pressure of steam used. Formulæ incorporating the best method for ascertaining the power developed, etc., are to be found in most manuals on the subject.

Tractive Effort.

It will suffice to give a brief definition of the term tractive effort, or "tractive force," as the power which a locomotive can exert at the tread of the driving wheels in its work of moving the load. The internal resistance, or friction, of the locomotive itself is usually neglected in determining this power, although allowance must ultimately be made, sufficient not only to overcome this but also to enable the engine to meet exceptional calls on its power for adverse conditions of weather, track, etc.

The actual formula is simple, and easily applied:

D = diameter of the cylinders in inches.
S = stroke of the pistons in inches.
p = mean effective pressure on the pistons in lbs. per sq. in.
W = diameter of driving wheels in inches.

T = the tractive force of the engine in lbs., or $T = \dfrac{D^2 S p}{W}$.

The locomotive illustrated in our coloured frontispiece has been chosen as a representative example of first-class British practice, and if the chief dimensions are taken and the above formula applied, the tractive effort can be easily found, and will assist the reader in following the remarks above.

The cylinders, of which there are four, are each $16\frac{1}{2}$ in. diameter by 26 in. stroke, whilst the driving wheels are 6 ft. 7 in. diameter. The boiler pressure is 220 lbs. per sq. in., and of this 85 per cent. is assumed to be effective in the cylinders:

Diameter of Cylinders.		Stroke.		Mean effective Pressure, 85 per cent. of 220 lbs. = 187.	Approx.

$$T = \frac{16 \cdot 5 \text{ in.}^2 \times 26 \text{ in.} \times 187}{79 \text{ in.}} \quad 17{,}000 \text{ lbs.,}$$

but as the engine has four cylinders, this must be doubled and the equation becomes:

$$2\left(\frac{D^2 S p}{W}\right) = 2 \times 17{,}000 = 34{,}000 \text{ lbs. tractive power.}$$

For compound locomotives, the equation becomes a little more complex, as the ratio (R) of the areas of the L.P. and H.P. pistons must be taken into consideration. For a two-cylinder compound the formula is $T = \dfrac{D i^2 S p}{(R+1)W}$, and a four-cylinder compound $T = \dfrac{2 D i^2 S p}{(R+1)W}$.

Di, diameter of L.P. cylinders; R, ratio of areas of pistons; L.P., H.P. and P, initial pressure in L.P. cylinder in lbs. per sq. in.

The tractive force obtained from these figures is somewhat limited in its application, for the mean effective pressure must be influenced by the speed of the pistons; and, further, it assumes the boiler pressure to be sufficiently maintained to make the calculated effective pressure in the cylinders available. Eighty-five per cent. is usually taken as a constant, although this is by no means universal.

Manifestly, it is an advantage to secure as high an effective pressure in the cylinders as possible, and for this reason all the details—regulator, steam-pipes, valves, etc., through which the steam has to pass should be very carefully designed, and any obstruction liable to cause loss from condensation, friction, etc., should be eliminated.

Tractive force, as shown above, is directly proportional to the stroke of the cylinder and the square of the diameter; it is, therefore, clear that where a locomotive is expected to exert enough energy for starting heavy loads, rapidly accelerating suburban trains, etc., the diameter of the cylinders must be large in proportion to the stroke.

A locomotive may be somewhat badly affected by exposure of the surfaces of its cylinders aggravating condensation losses, and hence any advantage to be gained by keeping cylinders small in diameter and long in stroke should not be lost sight of. The latter allows of earlier cut-offs, which will be explained later.

Much can be said regarding the number and disposition of cylinders for a locomotive, but, assuming sufficient power can be obtained within the prescribed load limits, an engine with only two cylinders represents the simplest and favourite arrangement.

Disposition of Cylinders.

The advantages of placing cylinders inside the frames are:—protection from the cooling influence of exposure to the atmosphere and draught caused in running; steadier running, as there is less disturbance laterally; tends to longer life of tyres, etc.; transverse strength of engine framing; less castings required, and shorter steam-passages. For the location of the cylinders outside, claims are made of possible shortening of wheel-base; absence of a cranked axle, often considered a weak detail; more accessible motion with longer connecting rods, etc.

Having obtained the necessary tractive effort for the work required of a locomotive, it is necessary to secure the requisite adhesion on the rails by arranging for " coupling " or connecting up a sufficient number of driving wheels, under ample dead-weight, to prevent " slipping," or non-gripping of the rails, when steam is admitted to the cylinders and the motive power applied.

The total adhesive weight of the locomotive illustrated in the frontispiece is 62 tons, so that the ratio of adhesion to the tractive effort is approximately as 4 is to 1.

Conditions of Service.

Originally it was customary to rely on locomotives having only the adhesion of a single pair of driving wheels, as already noted, for working fast passenger trains in this country. So long as the weight of the trains hauled was limited, these engines were successful, and many notable examples could be quoted, but, with increased weight of trains, additional driving wheels had to be coupled up, and now four-wheeled coupled, or six-wheeled coupled have completely ousted the " single-wheeler." For lines with heavy grades, as also for the haulage of goods and mineral trains, it was early discovered that additional driving wheels, to utilize more effectually the weight of the engine, must be connected up to secure the necessary adhesion.

The distribution of the weight on the axles of a locomotive needs special care on the part of the designer, or an unsteady engine will result, with inefficient hauling power. Tank engines are generally more difficult to balance than tender, owing to the varying levels of the water in the tanks which will occur in running.

Train Resistance.

Consideration must now be given to the resistance experienced by a locomotive in hauling a train, as this must intimately concern the power required of the engine. What the exact amount of the resistance offered to a train is, has been the subject of discussion, and various formulæ have been devised for estimating it. The state of the permanent way, the speed and direction of the wind, the velocity of the train, and the condition and load on the various bearings must seriously affect the matter. Train resistance must provide for all the above, leaving out for other consideration the forces due to gravity, as in ascending or descending an incline or curvature of the rails. Journal friction is felt most at starting, and will amount to from 15 to 18 lbs. per ton of the load, whilst as the speed increases, this will fall to from 2 to 4 lbs. per ton, when everything is at its best. The following gives the estimated resistance obtained from accepted formulæ:

TABLE I

Speed in miles per hour	10	30	50	60
Resistance in lbs. per ton—				
For a 4-coupled engine and tender	9·88	15·05	23·45	28·85
„ 6-coupled engine and tender	11·74	17·50	26·50	32·4
„ 8-coupled engine and tender	18·55	31·18	..	..
„ 4-wheeled wagon	4·57	8·15	13·89	17·56
„ bogie passenger coach	4·09	6·47	10·64	13·39

The above appertains to resistance on a level, straight track. Naturally, any ascending grade or incline will have a very important effect, and cause the resistance to traction to go up; this is shown by reference to the following:

TABLE II

Grade of 1 in					50	60	80	100
or					2%	1·6%	1·2%	1%
Resistance of engine, tender and train in lbs. per ton					44·8	37·3	28·0	22·4

The application of these to the example of a train of passenger vehicles totalling 500 tons in weight, hauled by a locomotive and tender taring 110 tons is interesting:

On a level and straight road, at 30 miles per hour:

	Coaches.	Engine and Tender.
Resistance in lbs. per ton (as table) . . .	6·47	17·50
Resistance total for train	500 × 6·47 = 3,235	
Resistance total for engine and tender . .	110 × 17·50 = 1,925	
	Total . . 5,160	

On an incline of 1 in 100 ascending, or 1 per cent. at 30 miles per hour:

	Coaches.	Engine and Tender.
Resistance on level (as Table I)	6·47	17·50
Add resistance on incline (as Table II) 1 in 100 .	22·4	22·4
	28·87	39·90

Total for train . . . . 500 × 28·87 = 14,435
Total for engine and tender . . 110 × 39·9 = 4,389

Total . . 18,824

The resistance due to gravity is expressed as $R = \text{load} \times \sin \theta$ or in lb. per ton of load $R = 2240 \times \sin \theta$, where θ is the angle that the incline makes with the horizontal. For all practical purposes this can be taken from the rise shown on the line side as 1 in 224, or 1 in 300, *i.e.* for an incline of 1 in 224 we may take $\sin \theta$ as $\frac{1}{224}$; in so doing we have taken the base of the right-angled triangle instead of the hypotenuse (Fig. 2). Now $1/224 \times 2240$ gives 10 lbs. per ton of load for grade resistance on an incline of 1 in 224.

The extra resistance of a train on a curve is usually neglected as invariably a coincident reduction in speed takes place. In special cases, however, where curves are very severe and much in evidence, allowance must be made, as considerable additional resistance will be encountered, due to the slip of the wheels on the rails, the radial position of the axles necessitating wheels on the outer rails taking a longer course than those on the inner.

By way of further illustrating the general construction of a modern locomotive, a photographic reproduction of a sectional model of a two-

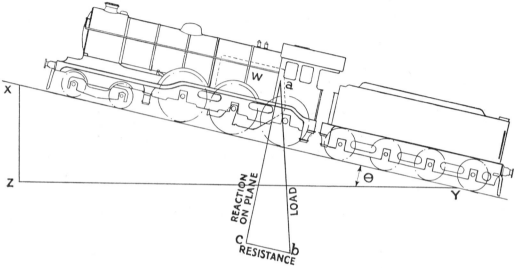

FIG. 2.—INCLINE RESISTANCE DIAGRAM.

cylinder o o O O o express locomotive is appended (Fig. 3). This shows in a very effective manner the interior of a boiler, details of the superheater, and general arrangements of the cylinder valves and running gear. A study of this will enable many details herein referred to being easily followed.

Weight Distribution.

In considering the design of a locomotive for any required service, it is most desirable that due consideration should be given to the distribution of weights in the finished machine. A well-balanced distribution of weight on the axles of a locomotive is a matter which requires simple, but tedious calculations on the part of the designer. The method usually adopted in the case of a new design is to calculate the position of the centre of gravity from estimated weights, and then by a method of trial and error so to adjust matters as to give the desired distribution. A practical knowledge of the requirements and conditions is, of course, necessary to guide the designer in his work.

Tank engines are generally more difficult to balance than tender engines because the weight in working order of a tank engine varies more than the weight in similar trim of a tender engine, owing to the varying loads of fuel and water in the coal bunkers and tanks of the first-mentioned type.

In the case of four-wheeled tank engines, the most desirable distribu-

FIG. 3.—SECTIONAL MODEL OF 4-6-2 PACIFIC LOCOMOTIVE, INDIAN STATE RYS.

tion of weight would be to have an equal load upon each axle; but this can seldom be obtained in practice for the reason already given.

Fig. 4 is an outline of a four-wheeled saddle-tank engine. The resultant centre of gravity of the locomotive, including water in the boiler, fuel on grate, water in tank, fuel in bunkers and men on footplate, should be about midway between the two pairs of wheels, and should not vary materially from this position with the water tanks and coal bunkers empty. The spring-borne weights are divided into sections, and the centre of gravity of each section is calculated and can be plotted down on a diagram of the engine. If the resultant centre of gravity does not work out in the desired position, then either the placing of the axles must be altered or a change made in the relative positions, say, of the water tank and coal bunkers, or, as a last resource, dead weight can be added in front or at the back to bring about a balance. It will now be understood that the position of the centre of gravity in a four-wheeled engine fixes the loads upon each axle, and no adjustment of the springs or addition of equalizing beams will have the slightest effect in modifying these weights. In the case of engines having three or more axles, the loads on each axle may be varied within certain limits independently of the position of the centre of gravity; but to obtain equal loads on each driving axle, which is undoubtedly the most desirable system of loading, there can only be one position for the centre of gravity relatively to the axles. It may therefore be taken as a rule applicable to all types of locomotives that where equal loads are required upon the driving axles, and certain predetermined loads required on the truck axles, then for any arrangement of wheel-base there can be only one position for the centre of gravity, and thus, as in the case of the four-wheeled engine, no amount of adjustment of springs or addition of equalizing beams will enable the weights to be fairly distributed if the centre of gravity is in the wrong place.

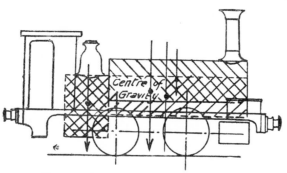

FIG. 4.—CENTRE OF GRAVITY DIAGRAM.

Centre of Gravity.

One of the most convenient ways of working out problems regarding the position of the centre of gravity is to assume a datum line in front of the locomotive and work out all the moments from this line. In a new design the weights of every portion will have to be calculated, and the distance of their separate centres of gravity estimated, from the datum line. These detail parts may then be grouped into larger sections so as to reduce the number of figures in the final calculations. The following case, taken from practice, shows the method.

Fig. 5 shows a 4-6-2 type of locomotive, without tender; and being of new design, before the figures shown thereon were finally settled, many adjustments had to be made to the wheel-base and relative position of the boiler.

The datum line was assumed to be at the front end of the frame, 2 ft. 10 in. in front of the centre line of the leading truck wheel. The engine was fitted with a cow-catcher, and as this extended in front of the datum line it comes into the calculations as a minus quantity. Overleaf is a list of sections and details, with their weights, dimensions from datum line and moments worked out.

The sum of the moments divided by the total weight gives the distance of the centre of gravity of the whole mass from the datum line. To get the final loads on the rails at each axle there must be added to the above spring-borne weights the weights of the wheels and axles themselves, which, in the case of the locomotive under consideration, are given in the table on p. 12.

It will be noticed that a great weight rolls upon the track unsupported by springs, which for many reasons connected with the

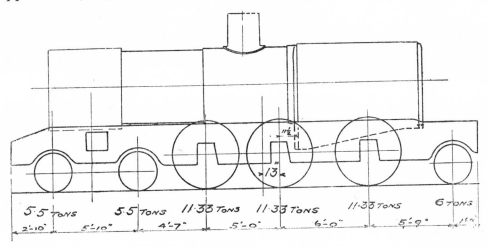

FIG. 5.—CENTRE OF GRAVITY DIAGRAM.

smooth running of the locomotive it is essential to keep as light as possible consistent with strength and safety.

Having determined the centre of gravity of the whole of the spring-borne weight, we have now to find the position of the axles to carry this weight. Usually there are a number of conditions to be met, which determine more or less the general design of the locomotive, even in the case of the most open specification.

The nature of the road-bed and strength of rails and bridges settles the weight which may not be exceeded on any one pair of wheels. The radius of the curves decides the maximum rigid wheel-base permissible, and also settles the amount of lateral play given to the truck wheels.

Bearing in mind all these points, as well as the practical ones connected with clearance of machinery, accessibility of parts, and convenience

Name of Part.	Centre of Gravity estimated from general drg. and measured from front end of Frame.	Calculated finished Weight of included Portion.	Moments.
	Ft.	*Cwt.*	
Smoke-box	4·75	37	176
Boiler barrel . .	13·625	216	2,950
Fire-box	23·08	217	5,050
Motion	10·5	34·5	392
Drag casting . .	30	21·5	645
Cab	28·5	32	915
Frames	15·25	50	765
Draw gear	0	5	0
Vacuum brake cylinder, etc. .	30	7·75	233
Sand-box	23·5	7·75	182
Cow-catcher . . .	·7	4·25	−3
Splashers, etc. . . .	18·25	14·75	270
Axle-boxes, slides and compensating beams . .	19	18	342
Cylinders and stretchers .	5·75	57·6	330
Rear buffing plate, etc. . .	31·75	4·5	143
Rear platform supports .	28·75	12·75	366
Running boards . . .	16	7·5	120
Fire-box frame stretcher .	17·5	2·5	44
Angle irons on frames . .	18	16·75	300
Front plate	2·5	1·85	4
Buffer plate and stretcher .	·5	5·75	3
Brake gear	20	13·75	275
		787	13,502

Four-wheeled bogie	54·5	cwt.
Leading coupled wheels and axle . . .	46·15	,,
Driving wheels and axle.	53·5	,,
Trailing and coupled wheels	46·12	,,
Trailing bogie	24·13	,,

and cheapness of manufacture, it is hardly possible to lay down any general rule which will enable the position of the wheels and axles to be determined, other than the rough-and-ready method of trial and error. With the help of a slide rule, however, it is surprising how quickly these matters can all be settled by one having the necessary experience.

Reverting to our example, Fig. 5, the position of the wheels and axles have all been determined after taking into account the above considerations.

A check on the results makes the centre of gravity of the whole locomotive 13 in. in front of the main driving axle, worked out as follows:

Weights (tons).	Distance from Datum.	Moments.
5·5	2·83	15·5
5·5	8·65	47·5
11·33	13·23	151·0
11·33	18·25	207·0
11·33	24·25	275·0
6	30	180·0
50·99		876·0

Distance from datum line to centre of gravity $\dfrac{876}{50\cdot99} = 17$ ft. 2 in.

Position of centre of gravity in relation to driving axle 18 ft. 3 in. − 17 ft. 2 in. = 13 in.

General Efficiency.

The maximum power of a steam locomotive depends entirely on the steam-producing capacity of the boiler. The fuel (amount and quality) used in a stated time is the limitation of that power, and over a given distance its commercial rating for traffic working. In the latter case the rating is stated either as " Pounds of fuel per mile," or " Pounds of fuel per ton mile." A better defined rating relative to the work done is, probably, " Pounds of fuel per horse-power per hour."

Locomotive engineering practice differs from almost all others, as it has no recognized standard of high economy for this rating, and for the sufficient reason that comparisons of the results from locomotives working under various load, speed and weather conditions involve calculations of a very complicated nature, further isolated experimental tests cannot be more than approximately true of average working conditions; so much depends on the men operating the machine. From the results of the latter method, however, it may be taken that $3\frac{1}{2}$ pounds of good English coal per horse-power per hour represents economical working under saturated steam conditions, this quantity being reduced to 2·1 or 2·2 pounds in the case of a well-designed superheated engine. With a high superheat (300° F.) the coal consumption has been reduced to as low as 1·8 lbs. 1 H.P. hour.

As an example of efficiency of a modern steam locomotive designed for fast passenger traffic the recorded results obtained on a trial run between London and Newcastle can be quoted. Hauling a train of

$375\frac{1}{2}$ tons a Pacific type locomotive " Papyrus " of the London and North Eastern Railway maintained an average speed of 70·4 m.p.h. for the 536·6 miles, inclusive of starting and stopping in both directions and all service reductions, and this on an average consumption of approximately 45 lbs. of South Yorkshire coal per mile, including lighting up. For over 12 miles an average speed of 100 m.p.h. was registered with a maximum of 108 m.p.h.

FIG. 6.—4–6–2 THREE-CYLINDER EXPRESS LOCOMOTIVE, NO. 2750 " PAPYRUS," L. & N.E.R.

The engine has three cylinders, 19in. diameter by 26 in. stroke, and driving wheels, 6 ft. 8 in. diameter, the boiler carries a working pressure of 220 lbs. per sq. in. Tractive force at 85 per cent., 32,909 lbs.

CHAPTER II

The Boiler—Its Construction—Types of Fire-boxes—Smoke-box arrangements—Regulators—
Fittings—Gauges—Lagging, etc.

Construction.

THE locomotive boiler in use to-day has been developed during years
of experience from the elementary boiler of similar fundamental construction adopted for George Stephenson's " Rocket," the famous and
successful competitor at the Rainhill trials of 1829. Briefly, it consists
of a horizontal, cylindrical barrel, with a rectangular fire-box at one
end and a suitable chamber at the other, forming a smoke-box—a series
of smoke-tubes uniting the two. Much attention has recently been
given to the production of an improved generator embracing the
principles of the water-tube boiler, and some interesting examples have
been built, and are in service, but, so far, the ordinary tubular type boiler
retains its pre-eminence.

Although this type of boiler is well adapted to its purpose, it cannot
be classed among the most efficient of steam producers, for, in the best
examples, only little more than 50 per cent. of the total heat generated
from the fuel burnt is actually transferred to the water evaporated, the
balance being lost by radiation, in waste gases, unconsumed ash, smoke,
etc. In evaporating properties, 8 lbs. of water per lb. of good steam-
coal consumed is considered a satisfactory return.

Fig. 1 shows in section a good specimen of a boiler of a modern
British locomotive. It will be seen that the barrel is traversed by a
number of smoke-tubes, which furnish a heating surface of some 1500
to 2000 sq. ft. The fire-box consists of a rectangular chamber, or
" inner " fire-box (usually of copper, in this country), wherein the
fire is accommodated. This is contained in an outer " shell " attached
to the main boiler barrel, and contributes another 200 sq. ft., or so,
to the heating surface; inner fire-boxes of steel are growing in favour.
At the opposite end of the barrel a smoke-box collects the products of
combustion drawn through the tubes by the action of the blast, and
from it they are finally ejected by way of the chimney. The boiler
barrel is now invariably built of special mild steel plates, of as large a

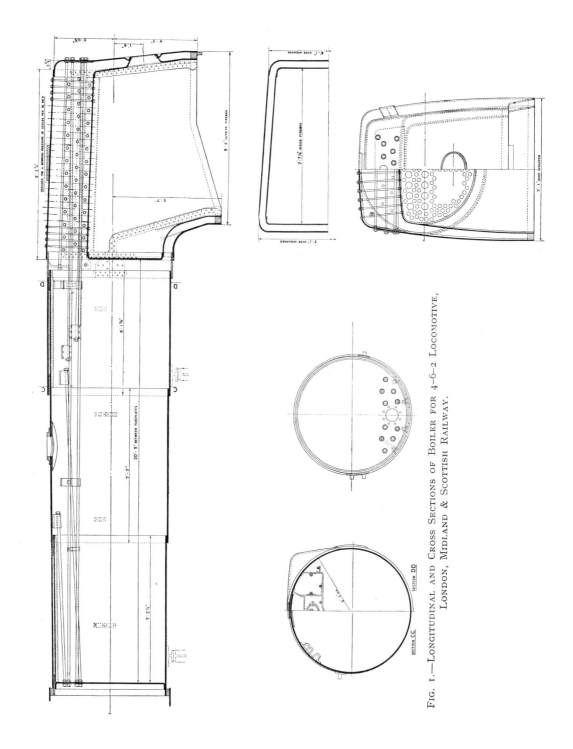

FIG. 1.—LONGITUDINAL AND CROSS SECTIONS OF BOILER FOR 4–6–2 LOCOMOTIVE, LONDON, MIDLAND & SCOTTISH RAILWAY.

superficial area as possible, to minimize the number of joints required in construction. Riveting is made, generally, with best Yorkshire iron rivets, closed by hydraulic machinery; the longitudinal seams are double-plated "butt" joints, whilst the circumferential ones are of "lap" form. Electric welding is now coming into favour for many of the joints of the outer fire-box and barrel.

In modern boilers the cylindrical body is often of tapering form (as Fig. 1), which enables the size of the fire-box to be somewhat increased, and the steam space in its vicinity to be of considerable capacity without adding unduly to the weight of the barrel, and of the water it contains. Further, this construction allows of greater advantage being taken of the heating surfaces of the fire-box and of the tubes, where they are of maximum value. A steam dome is usually arranged half-way along the barrel, but this has at the present time to be of very limited height in this country, as the loading-gauge of the railways does not permit of higher construction. When provided—although it may be of insignificant height—it gives the desired space in which to accommodate the regulator, internal steam-pipes, etc., as well as acting as a man-hole for access to the interior of the boiler during construction or repair.

Inner Fire-box.

The inner fire-box is stayed to the outer by a number of stays screwed into the plates, and either riveted over or expanded, after fixing. In the case of a copper inner fire-box, the stays are usually of copper; in a steel one they are generally of soft iron. The inner fire-box is dropped into the outer when the latter is turned upside down, and it is then fixed in position by riveting round the foundation ring. The roof of the fire-box is strengthened, or stayed, to resist pressure by an arrangement of direct stays passing from the top to the shell, or, in locomotives of moderate size, by girder stays fastened to it and suspended from the shell. Each system has its advantages, but the direct stay is the more popular now, as with this the roof of the fire-box is more easily kept clean. When the outer shell has a flat surface, or is of Belpaire type (Fig. 2), it will be seen how well it lends itself to direct staying; but when it is round and not too large perhaps, the method of laying longitudinal girders along the length of the fire-box and supporting these from the crown of the outer shell becomes a more practical proposition. This problem of staying the internal fire-box, or tying it to the outer, is one of much importance, and has had considerable attention devoted to it by designers. It is found in practice that it is undesirable to tie the inner fire-box too rigidly, or strains may be set up, due to differences in expansion and contraction, which will seriously affect the joints; it is desirable to allow as much flexibility as possible, consistent with safety.

The front tube-plate and the back-plate of the outer fire-box are either tied to each other (being directly opposed) or stayed from the boiler barrel.

Belpaire Fire-box.

The drawing (Fig. 2) illustrates a large boiler with a Belpaire fire-box, and shows the longitudinal stays of iron, or steel, running the

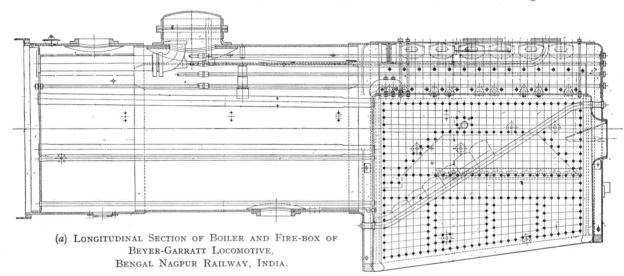

(a) Longitudinal Section of Boiler and Fire-box of
Beyer-Garratt Locomotive,
Bengal Nagpur Railway, India.

full length of the barrel, screwed into the back-plate. The holes have fine threads to allow the stays, also screwed at the front ends, to pass readily through. They are then screwed into the front tube-plate, as introduced, and held by having a nut on each side of the tube-plate, to form a steam-tight joint with copper washers; the plate is faced back and front to enable this joint to be formed.

The staying at the tube-plate end of the fire-box is specially designed to ensure flexibility there.

Stays.

The drawing also shows the staying of the inner fire-box to the outer, with copper stays

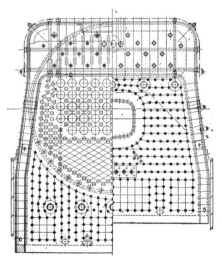

(b) Cross Sections of Boiler.

Fig. 2.

placed about 4 in. apart, screwed in and riveted over at both ends to form heads. The flat side surfaces of the inner and outer fire-boxes which require staying are of considerable area, totalling on a modern locomotive between 100 and 120 sq. ft.

The distance apart of the stays has long since been settled by practical experience and consideration of construction, and it will be found that for the last half-century the pitch of side stays of a fire-box has remained in the neighbourhood of 4 in. Accordingly it may be assumed that the number of stays required per square foot is nine, and that a fire-box plate area—including the back-plate and the two sides of the wrapper-plate—of usual dimensions, will require, approximately, 1000 stays. Assuming a working pressure of 180 lbs. per sq. in., with stays at 4 in. pitch, each supporting approximately 16 sq. in., it will be seen that the total tensile stress on each stay is 2880 lbs.

There are many circumstances to be taken into consideration apart from the true tensile stress on the stay section in the water space. Many designs of stays are reduced in diameter—or, alternatively, reduced in section by means of saw-cuts—between the fire-box plates, in order to provide for a certain amount of flexibility; and when this minimum section is taken into account it is generally agreed that the maximum stress in tension of any material should not exceed 6000 lbs. per sq. in. Accordingly the section at the weakest point for stays pitched at 4 in. with a boiler pressure of 180 lbs. should be one-half of a square inch, or of a diameter of 0.798 in. That is when copper is used. Other materials in use for stays of higher tensile strength than copper are frequently allowed a greater stress than above, but not in proportion to the increased tenacity.

The materials employed are (1) copper, (2) copper alloy, (3) bronzes of various composition, (4) soft steel, and (5) high-class puddled iron. Copper, at one time, was all but standard in Europe, but now, owing to economic stress, great attempts have been made to replace it with soft steel or iron.

Arguments pro and con regarding the advantages and disadvantages of the above could be introduced at considerable length, but only brief comment is necessary here. In the case of copper, the two main arguments against its use are (1) its first cost, and (2) its low tensile strength. The first is fairly obvious, but copper stays are not necessarily a bad investment, as scrap copper has a rather high value in proportion to its original price. The low tensile strength of copper is certainly important, but staybolts are not designed entirely on tensile strength, and the high ductility of copper presents many advantages for its use as side stays, which there is no doubt are subjected to a considerable amount of movement in certain parts of the fire-box, owing to expansion and contraction. Copper, in other words, is one of the soft and tough materials which are very useful in situations where non-rigid tie-bars are required, such as fire-box stays susceptible to wastage.

Fig. 3 gives the effect of temperature on copper bars, from which it will be seen that the normal tenacity of 14.5 tons per sq. in. becomes 12 tons per sq. in. at a temperature equal to steam at 200 lbs. pressure.

The objections urged against steel stays are (1) their possible corrosion, which can always take place, and (2) their inferior softness as compared with copper, which somewhat affects a repairing job in the shed. Cheapness of steel is its great inducement, and in practice

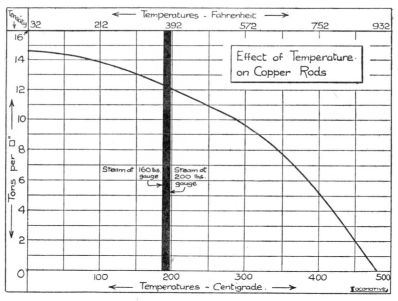

FIG. 3.

it certainly gives service with very little inferior results to that obtained from copper or bronze, although it is stated that the maintenance of fire-boxes with steel stays is apt to be higher than those with copper. Puddled iron of the best qualities is largely used and is less sensitive to corrosion than steel. Stays of this material are somewhat easier to rivet over than steel, but unless the iron is of excellent quality cracks are apt to develop. Further, the continual movement of the fire-box may tend to brittleness which leads to the stay snapping in service. The relative flexibility of a puddled-iron bar, however, has much in its favour, as it is equivalent in texture to a stranded wire rope, the iron being really an intermixture of iron fibres with slag fibres, which true fibrous characteristic is not present in either copper, bronze, or the usual qualities of soft steel. Fig. 4 shows a group of iron stays, bent and cut through to illustrate this fibrous character of the material.

Fig. 5 represents several forms of stay, non-flexible and semi-flexible. —SKETCH A. This shows the simplest form of stay, being merely a piece of threaded rod cut off to the varying lengths desired and headed over when in position. Any suitable material can be used, but more generally this simple stay is only employed in copper or bronze. Heads on the inner side are sometimes preferred larger and thicker than those on the outer side, in order to better resist the action of the fire.

SKETCH B illustrates a solid "flexible" stay, this quality being obtained by turning off the central screw-threads. Iron, steel, and copper are used in this form. The reduced central area minimizes the liability to breakage which is present when the harder materials are used and the maximum section is retained. In America certain railroads are employing stays in which this central portion is turned down to $\frac{1}{2}$ in. diameter, and the pitch of the stays proportionately decreased, in order to not exceed the maximum tensile stress.

THREADED COLD BEND
SAWN THROUGH AND ETCHED
TO SHOW UNIFORMITY OF STRUCTURE

By courtesy of N. Hingley & Sons, Ltd., Dudley.

FIG. 4.—IRON STAYS.

SKETCH C shows a form of hollow staybolt, with a blind hole, such staybolts being made as separate pieces, with one head formed. This has a square end for screwing the stay into the box, which end is usually chipped off after it has served its purpose. The hole detects a broken stay by the escape of water, and staybolts on this principle tend to become more generally used. The hole in this case is blind on the side of the inner fire-box, so that the water escape is through the wrapper side, holes being present in the lagging sheets coincident with each stayhead. This prevents any quenching of the fire, and also prevents the admission of air should a number of broken stays be present—and is also obviously more observable. The provision of hundreds of holes in the lagging plates, and also the need of their being fixed reasonably opposite the staybolts every time the plates are removed is, however, somewhat of an objection.

SKETCH D. On the fire-box side the staybolt heads wear with comparative rapidity owing to erosion caused by the fuel and gases. It is clearly very necessary to maintain a head of some dimension in order to protect the joint of screw-thread and plate, and a renewable head is shown here—this consisting of a screwed metal cap inserted into a drilled and tapped hole in the end of the worn stay.

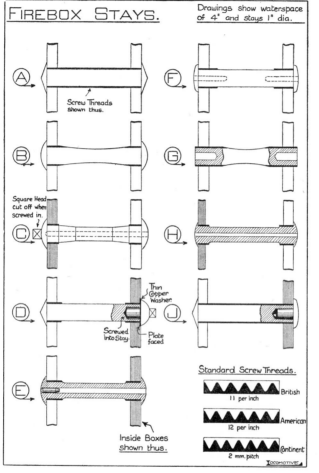

FIG. 5.

SKETCH E shows a hollow staybolt, reduced in middle length, and plugged at the wrapper end. Such staybolts are frequently made as hollow bars, and the plug is employed so that the water emitted by a broken bolt may come into the fire-box side only, and not also between the shell and the lagging, contrary to the intention in " C."

SKETCH F. Herein is shown a form of staybolt with an elliptical head, which provides the maximum thickness over the joint circumference of the usual practical shapes. This staybolt is drilled down from each end, and shows the general Central European standard.

SKETCH G illustrates a steel stay, reduced centrally, and having no cupped head, the stay being made steam-tight by driving a conical plug into each end. This is not used largely to-day, as no protection is given to the thread at the junction with the plate.

SKETCH H. This is a usual form of stay in the U.S.A., where it is now compulsory to employ hollow bolts, and owing to the universal employment of steel and iron bolts with steel inner fire-boxes, it is now not an unusual practice to weld the heads to the sheet.

SKETCH J gives a form of renewable head which was introduced fifty years ago and which consists of a small turned piece which is driven into the inner end of the stay. When burnt or eroded, this end is intended to be readily replaceable, but the method has not come into extended use, that shown at " D " being preferable.

With regard to hollow staybolts, such as at " H," it was held in some quarters that, apart from their quality as detectors, they assisted combustion by the admission of air over the fire. The idea has been carried to extreme by short pieces of boiler tube being used as stays on the midway rows. It is fairly clear, however, that two disadvantages are speedily presented by any attempt to assume stays as air conduits, namely, (1) the fact that the air supply is uncontrollable by practical means, and (2) that the holes, whether small or large, will gradually choke with furnace residue.

A further assortment of staybolts is shown in Fig. 6, to which the following brief remarks apply:

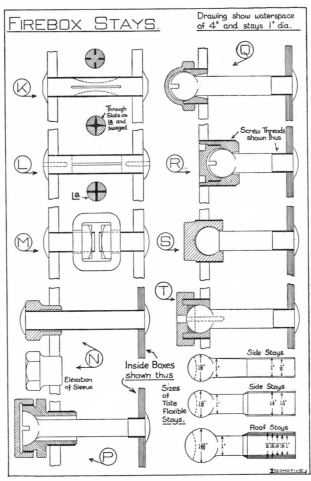

FIG. 6.

SKETCH K. In this form, the bolt is what might be termed the "semi-flexible" variety, four saw-cuts at right angles being made partially through the diameter as shown in the section. The head shown on this staybolt is of the German State Railways truncated cone form.

SKETCH L shows a staybolt with the slits completely through, as indicated at " L " (a). The flexibility of this stay is good, but if the threading in the plates is very tight, it will tend to twist in the process of being inserted and cause difficulty. Accordingly, a later practice has been to cut the slots in the blank which has been parted from the rolled or drawn bar, and then to swage the blank under a light hammer, thus closing the slots, and giving rigidity against the torsion of screwing-in position, whilst not diminishing the flexibility in any way.

SKETCH M shows an early type of non-rigid staybolt, which was introduced in this country some decades ago. It cannot be regarded as a very satisfactory form, but provided the genesis of the idea. Certain difficulties in fitting it would appear to be present, but for the danger zone situations these would not be pronounced.

SKETCH N. Herein is shown one of the earliest types of bolts which was provided with a sleeve attachment screwed into the outer wrapper. This is not a flexible bolt, the sleeve being fitted simply to make available a longer stay and thereby diminish the risk of breakage. The scheme in principle is, however, the basis of the modern flexible bolt.

SKETCH P. This is one of the earliest designs of truly flexible bolts introduced. The home of this pattern of bolt is the U.S.A., owing to the large fire-boxes which are standard, and the later developments there are of great interest. In the present illustration it will be noted that a sleeve is screwed into the outer wrapper, and this has a spherical seating. The bolt-head matches, the bolt itself being screwed into the inner sheet by means of the saw-cut in the head. A flat cover making a steam-tight joint is then screwed over the sleeve. One disadvantage of this form is the length of the sleeve, which can scale both inside and outside; the deposit may interfere with the free working of the bolt in time.

SKETCH Q shows the well-known " Tate " staybolt, which is probably the most widely used of any true flexible form. The head is truly spherical, and bears on a small sleeve which has no threads exposed to the water, and a large tapered clearance space. A neat cap screw over the whole provides a good practical job.

SKETCH R. Herein is shown the same form of staybolt, but the " flush-sleeve " type, so that no interference is presented with the seating of any fittings needed on the wrapper sheets.

SKETCH S. This is an extremely neat type, in which the sleeve is drop-forged over the spherical head, and the whole combination simultaneously screwed into position.

SKETCH T shows a flexible staybolt with a tell-tale in the end. For this purpose it is necessary to mechanically pack the head, and a metallic packing is accordingly used as shown.

Smoke-tubes.

Smoke-tubes can be either of copper, brass, iron, or steel—usually the last named at the present time, due to dictates of economy. They are as a rule about 2 in. in outer diameter, and of metal 1/16 in. thick. They are nearly parallel throughout their length except at the smoke-box end, where they are expanded out to about 1/16 in. larger in diameter. This, in conjunction with the holes in the smoke-box tube-plate being made rather larger than those in the fire-box tube-plate, enables the tubes to be easily introduced from that end. To fasten them in the tube-plates, they are opened out or " expanded " by an expander having hard steel rollers arranged round a spindle or mandrel (see Fig. 7). At the fire-box end they are beaded over as well at *a* (Fig. 8), and a ferrule *b* driven in to ensure tightness. With steel fire-boxes the tubes are now frequently welded to the tube-plates, which forms a very tight connection (Fig. 9).

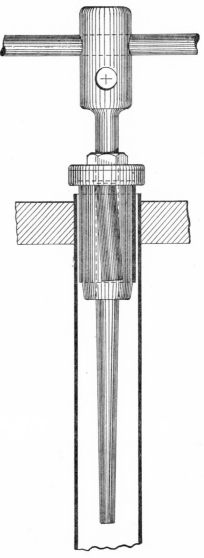

FIG. 7.—TUBE EXPANDER.

The arrangement of tubes in the tube-plates offers another problem to the designer, who naturally is keen to secure the greatest efficiency: they can either be arranged in vertical rows, or in diagonal lines, vertical and horizontal. Each method has its supporters; the first enables the tubes to be kept cleaner externally, whilst the second gives better facilities for the rising bubbles of steam to leave the evaporating surfaces. Further, the latter arrangement gives a stronger surface for the tube-plates, there being more metal left between the holes, to form " bridges," as they are termed. Fig. 9A illustrates these lay-outs.

The " throat " plate of the outer fire-box, which is that connecting the lower portion with the barrel of the boiler, is a somewhat complicated detail, and has to be flanged in two opposite directions—the upper side outwards, towards the front of the boiler barrel, whilst the lower flanges have to be inwards, to connect with the wrapper plate of the outer shell. It is usually produced in a hydraulic press, and the flanges should have a large radii, otherwise cracking along the corner may happen. In the assembly of a locomotive boiler, great care must be exercised to see that all joints are in good alignment and the holes perfectly opposite.

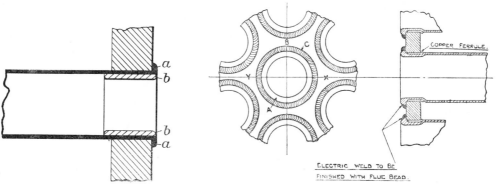

FIG. 8.—EXPANDED TUBE END.   FIG. 9.—WELDED TUBE END.

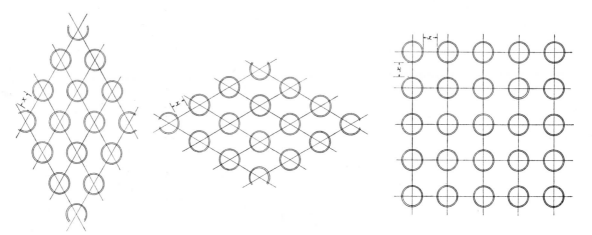

(a) VERTICAL DIAMOND.   (b) HORIZONTAL DIAMOND.   (c) MARINE OR RECTANGULAR.

FIG. 9A.—LAY-OUT OF TUBE-PLATES.

The foundation ring at the bottom of the fire-box to which the inner and outer boxes are riveted is either a forging of wrought iron or a steel casting. It should be machined to exact dimensions, and the rivet-holes through it accurately marked off to meet those of the fire-box plates. It is customary when boilers are assembled for all parts to be held in place temporarily while the rivet-holes are checked over for correct alignment.

Steel Fire-boxes.

The relative advantages of copper or steel for the construction of these have been much debated, but, with the enormous number in satisfactory service in America, South Africa, etc., there can be little doubt that fire-boxes of steel plates can be, and are, under the conditions

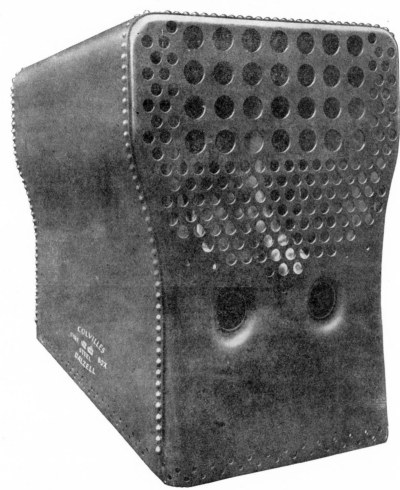

FIG. 10.—AN ALL-STEEL FIRE-BOX MADE BY THE VULCAN FOUNDRY LTD., AND EQUIPPED WITH THERMIC SYPHONS.

in which they give service, as satisfactory as those of copper. Fig. 10 gives a steel fire-box of British manufacture, which may be taken as an example of the very latest practice. As will be seen from the drawing (Fig. 11) reproduced, the inside box is composed of three plates, viz. a back, or fire-door plate, a front tube-plate, with a wrapper-plate, forming the sides and crown. In this case, the joints are riveted, but it is common practice now to electrically weld them.

Another detail must be mentioned—the provision of a pair of "thermic syphons" in the combustion chamber. These provide additional heating surface, thereby assisting towards a better circulation of the water in the boiler. These thermic syphons are very popular in America, and a large number are in use in the Colonies and in India.

The employment of steel for fire-boxes is claimed to reduce the first cost of locomotives by eliminating high-priced copper, as well as appreciably decreasing the dead-weight, as the steel used is much thinner

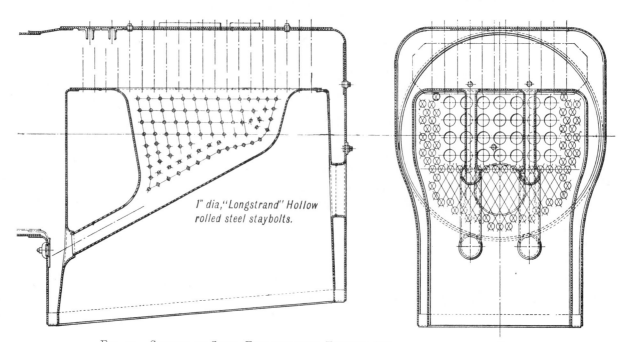

I" dia, "Longstrand" Hollow rolled steel staybolts.

FIG. 11.—SECTION OF STEEL FIRE-BOX WITH THERMIC SYPHONS, AS SHOWN IN FIG. 10.

than copper would be; also the steel stays used with the steel plate are smaller in diameter. It is predicted, too, that higher pressure can be arranged for without increasing the cost of maintenance.

Fire-brick Arch.

A fire-brick arch is usually arranged in the fire-box, whereby any unconsumed gases from the burning coal are obliged to pass over highly-heated refractory surfaces prior to entering the smoke-tubes, thus giving good combustion. Fig. 12 shows an example constructed of fire-brick shapes or blocks dove-tailed together and supported on angles secured to the inner fire-box plate.

Fire-grates.

Fire-grates in this country are " inclined " or " horizontal," according to the class of coal used as fuel. The position of the axles, too, in a locomotive often influences the style of grate, it being necessary to

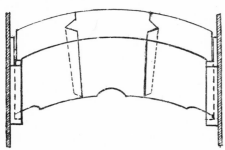

FIG. 12.—FIRE-BRICK ARCH.

provide an inclined grate in many cases where the rear axle of an engine is one of the coupled variety. With small, dusty, fast-burning coal, the horizontal grate is claimed to give the best results; with slow-burning Welsh coal, or semi-anthracite, an inclined grate possibly secures most favour. The latter mostly slant from the trailing end towards the front at an inclination of about 1 in 10. Although rocking grates are rarely used on British locomotives, with their comparatively short runs, there is much to be said for them in countries where long runs are the rule, and indifferent fuel has to be used. The area of the grate will range from 20 sq. ft. to 45 sq. ft. and more, dependent on the size of the locomotive and grade of coal to be used.

Fire-bars.

The actual form given to fire-bars as a rule is the longitudinal spacing, the bars being packed closer together, or wider apart, to suit the particular coal used. An im-

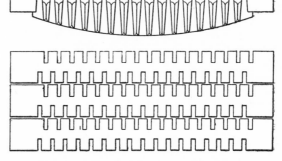

FIG. 13.—COLLINS' IMPROVED FIRE-BARS.

proved form giving more stability to the bar is shown in Fig. 13, wherein each bar consists of a central web having windage slots made by vertical ribs tapering downward from the surface. These ribs are " staggered " relatively to each other, and extend to the full depth of the bar. Even draught is ensured through the entire length and breadth of any fire-box fitted with these. The ribs are chamfered at the surface edge to secure good fitting. Bars can be reversed independently without others being affected.

Correct draught is important if complete combustion of fuel is to be attained, and the air spaces in this case have been proportioned to secure efficient combustion by the distribution of the air uniformly throughout the grate.

Ashpans.

Below the grate an ashpan is provided which has dampers operated from the footplate to control the entrance of air. Figs. 14 and 15 illustrate such ashpans, the second having two dampers and a dividing plate.

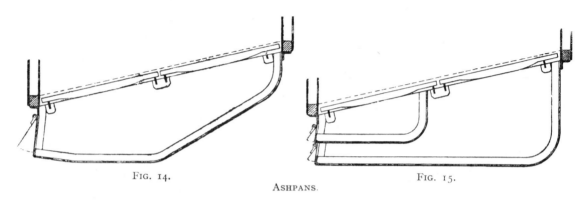

FIG. 14.

ASHPANS.

FIG. 15.

Smoke-boxes.

The smoke-box, or "front-end," accommodates the steam-pipes, etc., and forms a convenient method of collecting the smoke and gases after these have passed the boiler tubes. It used to be the custom to determine the length of the smoke-box by the length of the cylinders, but now it generally assumes a more extended form, as it has been found that a smoke-box of larger capacity tends to steady and equalize the draught through the tubes. Further, it provides more area for the spark arrestor, superheater connections, etc.

Blast-pipes.

The blast-pipe arranged in the smoke-box acts as a powerful inducing apparatus, and can be found in a great variety of forms. The position of the blast orifice relative to the tubes and chimney has been subject to innumerable experiments. Diagram (Fig. 16) gives four typical examples taken from British, Indian and foreign practice. The relative dimensions adopted are as follows:

	D	d	h	b	P	p
Fig. 1.	69 in.	17 in.	3 in.	25 in.	$12\frac{3}{4}$ in.	9 in.
Fig. 2.	$51\frac{1}{2}$ in.	$13\frac{1}{4}$ in.	1 in. up	18 in.	4 in.	$10\frac{1}{2}$ in.
Fig. 3.	$67\frac{5}{8}$ in.	14 in.	. .	24 in.	24 in.	10 in.

With a much lower position of nozzle a "petticoat"-pipe, or draught-pipe, is usually interposed between the nozzle and the chimney. The proper size of the nozzle for any particular engine is determined more by experience and tests in practice than by any fixed rule; its diameter averages one-fourth that of the cylinders.

Methods of varying the diameter of the nozzle to meet different conditions of service, grades of fuel, etc., are very numerous, and much adopted in countries where it is desirable to have a variable blast. Here the tendency is to adhere to a fixed nozzle of a dimension which gives the most general satisfaction, as it has been proved that all movable devices in the smoke-box are unreliable in service, owing to the corrosion, violent expansion and accumulation of dirt to which they are subject.

Spark Arrestors.

Spark arrestors of either deflecting plates or steel wire netting are common in smoke-boxes, especially where lignite fuel or wood is being used. The position is arbitrarily fixed by experience.

The emission of sparks from chimneys of locomotives has long been a subject of complaint, and there is no doubt much damage can

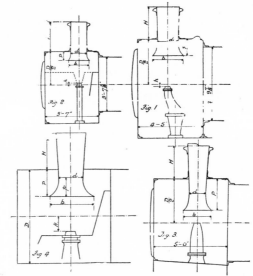

FIG. 16.—BLAST-PIPE DIAGRAM.

be done alongside the track during spells of dry weather. The illustration (Fig. 17) shows an ingenious arrangement which has lately had some application on French railways. Two, or more, series of inclined parallel steel strips form baffle-plates, the inclination of the plates of one being inverse to that of the other. In the detail the plates are so arranged that the end B of plate AB of the first series is between the ends C and E of the adjacent plates of the second, so that the consumed gases follow the path shown by the arrow F. In operation the gases carrying incandescent sparks follow the direction of the arrow H. Under the effect of the blast, the sparks follow the arrow I, hit the second series of plates, which breaks them up and they become extinguished as they fall. The lower diagram gives a modified form in which a series of plates are arranged to form a truncated cone surrounding the blast-pipe.

Soot Cleaners.

Owing to the difficulty of access to modern locomotive smoke-boxes for cleaning the tubes, etc., a device known as a soot cleaner can be permanently applied to the fire-box front. Fig. 18 shows a successful form, which is arranged in a tube passing through the water space at the back of the fire-box above the fire-door. Three independent steam jets are provided in the nozzle, so adjusted that they will cover the whole area of the tube-plate when in use. The valve is self-contained, and works instantaneously by the action of a trigger controlling the pilot valve. It is claimed that this device secures an economy of 50 per cent. in steam for its operation as compared with other methods. When in use, one revolution of the handle is sufficient to direct the steam jets over the whole of the surface of the tube-plate, cleaning the tubes and removing any deposit whilst the engine is in service.

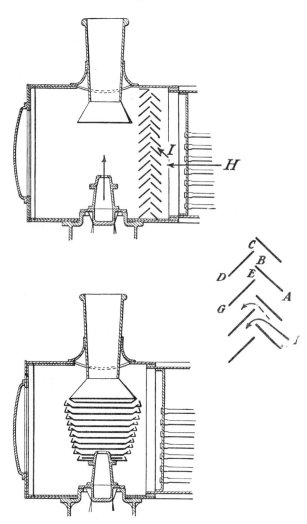

FIG. 17.—SPARK ARRESTORS.

Feed Injectors.

As the boiler generates steam which is to be used in the engine, so must water be supplied to replace that evaporated, and for this purpose the simplest device is a steam injector; and satisfactorily to assist in the explanation of the working of this, Fig. 19 is given, wherein the connections for steam and water and the feed-delivery to the boiler are shown. The operation of an injector depends entirely on the velocity

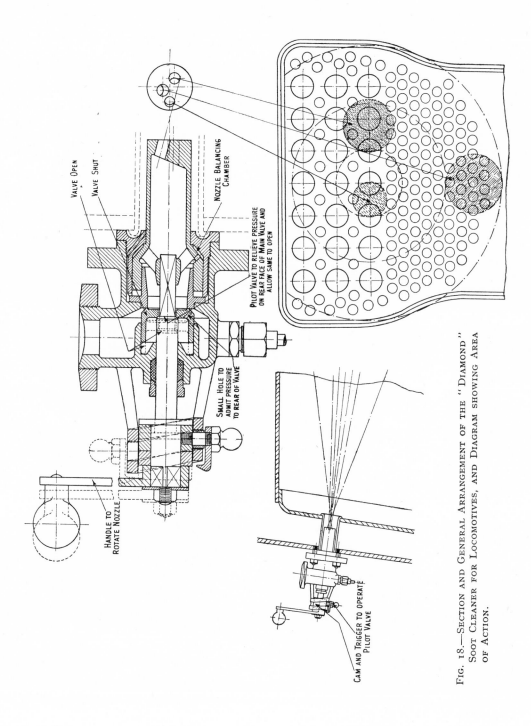

VALVE OPEN

VALVE SHUT

NOZZLE BALANCING CHAMBER

PILOT VALVE TO RELIEVE PRESSURE ON REAR FACE OF MAIN VALVE AND ALLOW SAME TO OPEN

SMALL HOLE TO ADMIT PRESSURE TO REAR OF VALVE

HANDLE TO ROTATE NOZZLE

CAM AND TRIGGER TO OPERATE PILOT VALVE

FIG. 18.—SECTION AND GENERAL ARRANGEMENT OF THE "DIAMOND" SOOT CLEANER FOR LOCOMOTIVES, AND DIAGRAM SHOWING AREA OF ACTION.

imparted to the feed-water by the sudden condensation of steam. High-velocity steam passing through the combining nozzle is suddenly condensed by the water induced from the tank, and the combined jet then rushes forward through the smaller nozzle and clack-valve to the boiler, overcoming the pressure therein by the velocity imparted to it. It is the transformation of energy taken from the high velocity of the steam and imparted to the low velocity of the water entering by the feed that enables the injector to deliver water into the boiler at the same, or even higher, pressure than the steam it receives.

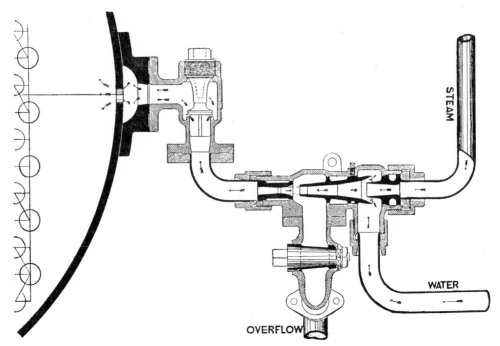

FIG. 19.—INJECTOR IN ACTION.

Fig. 20 shows the actual construction of a modern restarting, lifting injector, whilst 20A illustrates the steam-valve actuated by the overflow.

Injectors working with the exhaust steam are now much used, and these will receive due attention in the chapter devoted to feed-water heating, etc.

Feed-pumps.

In cases where a pump driven from a reciprocating detail of the motion is used, this is generally arranged in a convenient position on the framing of the engine, and Fig. 21 shows in detail such a pump, while Fig. 22 gives its position and general arrangement on the frame.

Feed Clacks and Delivery.

Another important detail is the feed-water " clack " (or non-return valve), by which the feed-water is admitted to the boiler. A favoured position is now on the upper portion of the boiler barrel, with trays inside the boiler to distribute the entering water. There is much to be said for this arrangement, as the feed-water is raised to a very high temperature before actually mingling with that already in the boiler, and a more equal distribution is assured, thus obviating local cooling of the surfaces of the boiler or tubes adjacent to the feed entrance. Fig. 23 illustrates the arrangement as applied to a boiler.

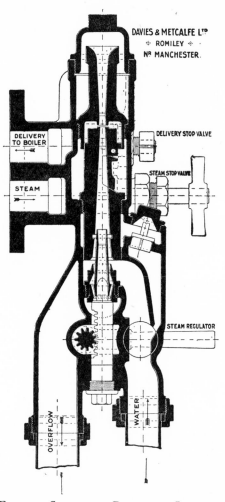

Water-gauges.

It is customary to provide a couple of water-gauges, usually fitted with automatic valves for closing the passages from the boiler to prevent escape of steam or water

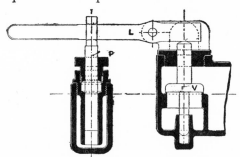

FIG. 20A.—AUTOMATIC STEAM VALVE
ACTUATED BY THE OVERFLOW.

FIG. 20.—SECTION OF RESTARTING INJECTOR.

if the gauge glass gets accidentally broken. Fig. 24 illustrates an excellent example in its approximate position, on the fire-box front. It is equipped with plate-glass protectors and ball valves, which will close when any abnormal rush of steam or water takes place.

A type of water-gauge for use on locomotive boilers with very high pressure is illustrated in Fig. 25, where the glass tube is replaced by a metal body having a plate-glass front held tightly in place against the

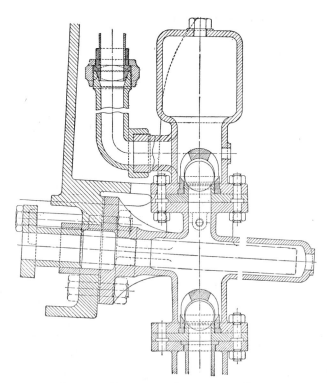

FIG. 21.—DETAILS OF LONG-STROKE PUMP.

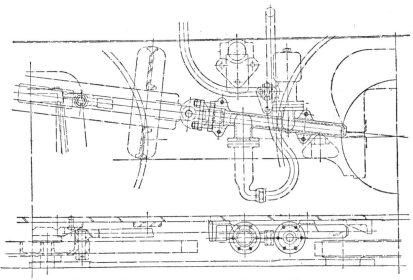

FIG. 22.—ORDINARY LONG-STROKE PUMP IN POSITION.

body by the pressure within. A reflector plate is arranged behind the water, so that the level is distinctly seen.

Fusible Plugs.

As a protection against overheating of the inner fire-box in cases of failure of the feed, and consequently low water, a fusible plug is provided, screwed into the plate forming the roof of the fire-box. The central core of this is made of lead alloy, which will readily melt and give warning if overheated before damage is done to the plate.

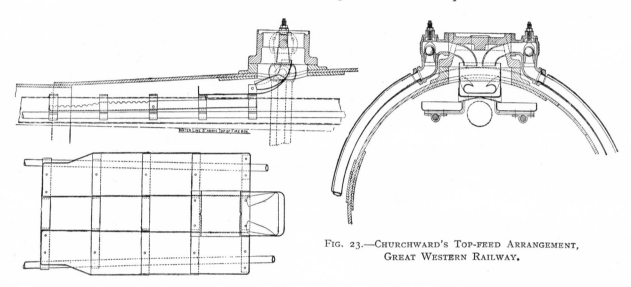

FIG. 23.—CHURCHWARD'S TOP-FEED ARRANGEMENT, GREAT WESTERN RAILWAY.

Safety Valves.

Another important fitting is, of course, the safety-valve, and this to-day is generally of the " Pop " spring-loaded type. Figs. 26 and 26A show approved patterns which cannot be tampered with. The valve of Fig. 26A is loaded with a spring which is so adjusted that the valve lifts immediately the working pressure is reached, and it shuts as soon as this is relieved. The valve is provided with an external lip, or rim, so that as the pressure raises it an increased area is presented to the action of the steam, ensuring a decided lift to relieve pressure. With the old-established Ramsbottom type of valve, Fig. 26, an increased pressure of from 5 to 10 lbs. of steam per sq. in. could easily be effected, although the valve might be blowing off; with approved Pop valves this is impossible.

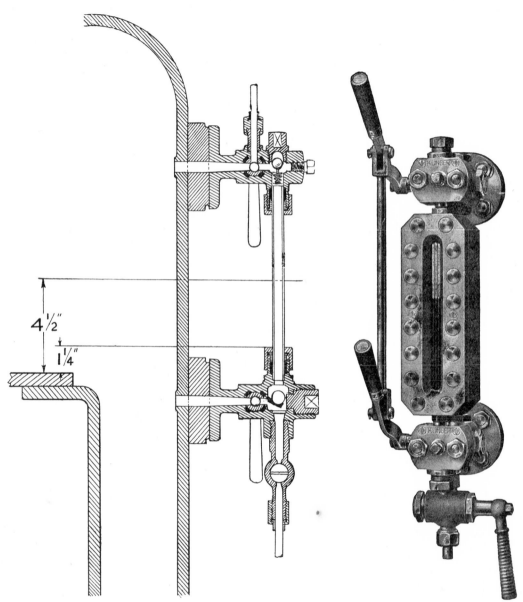

4½"

1¼"

FIG. 24.—WATER-GAUGE WITH AUTOMATIC BALL VALVES
IN POSITION ON FIRE-BOX FRONT (SECTION).

FIG. 25.—FRONT VIEW OF HIGH-
PRESSURE WATER-GAUGE.

Steam Turret.

A steam "turret" or "chamber," is also located above the fire-box, from which the steam used for the various auxiliary devices—injector-feeds, brake apparatus, steam-heat, whistle, etc., is taken. When provided with a suitable stop-valve, any of the attached controls can be attended to whilst the boiler is under steam—a proceeding sometimes necessary.

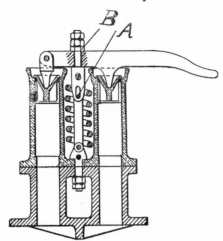

FIG. 26.—RAMSBOTTOM SAFETY-VALVE.
A = Pin connecting safety link.
B = Bolt holding spring to lever.

Regulators.

The regulator, or valve, by means of which the supply of steam from the boiler to the cylinders is controlled, is usually placed in the dome, with its inlet as high above the surface of the water in the boiler as possible. This condition, however, has nowadays become so difficult to meet, as already noted, that alternative procedure is common, and will be described later.

FIG. 26A.—"POP" SAFETY-VALVE.

The ordinary type of regulator used for many years past is of the flat, sliding design, and a good example is to be found in the locomotive illustrated in the frontispiece, which also clearly demonstrates the confined limits imposed by the British loading-gauge. The main valve—of brass—covers the ports in the cast-iron head of the steam-pipe, and has a second, and smaller, slide of brass to open and shut a port in its face. These valves are connected up to the regulator rod by a connecting rod, crank, and pin, the latter passing through a hole in the smaller valve, so that this is lifted at once if the regulator is moved to the open position; a similar hole in the large valve is slotted, so that this moves only after the smaller one has uncovered the port in it, thus relieving the pressure and enabling the main valve to be operated with less effort.

Another form of regulator, much in use, is of the double-beat type, balanced by presenting unequal surfaces to the steam pressure. Fig. 27

shows an approved valve of this type which is claimed to give efficient control of the steam, is easy to operate, and can be readily maintained tight and reliable in service.

It consists of a single sected main valve C formed with a cylindrical throttle extension D on its outlet side, and a piston on its steam side, containing an auxiliary pilot, or balancing, valve K, which terminates in a fine-pointed cone and is attached to the valve spindle E.

The piston, packed with an ordinary piston-ring, works in a cylindrical extension of the valve casing, and forms with it a balancing chamber A, which is in permanent communication with the boiler through the

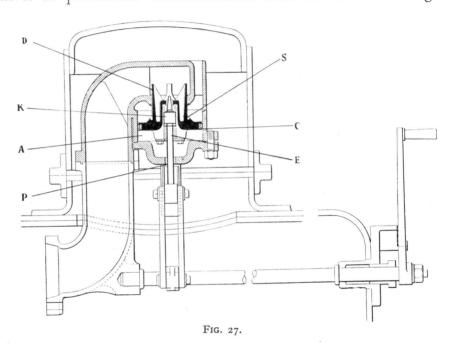

FIG. 27.

annular space P, and this is kept under steam pressure which, so long as the pilot valve K remains closed, presses the main valve firmly against its seat S.

When the pilot valve K is drawn from its seat within the main valve, it allows steam from the balancing chamber A to pass the conical point of the spindle until the rate of flow past the pilot valve K is in excess of the steam supply to it through the space P; the pressure in A is thereby reduced.

As soon as this occurs, the pressure below the piston is no longer able to resist the pressure above, with the result that it is forced down into the chamber A, and the main valve moves with it and allows steam to pass to the main steam-pipe. The main valve D adjusts its position with regard to the small pilot valve K, so that the flow of steam from the balancing chamber A, below the piston part of the large valve exactly equals the supply passing the space P. In this position it responds directly to the slightest movement of the small valve and spindle. The effort required to open this type of regulator is small, as the throttle valve is only one inch in diameter and is the only valve directly operated by the movement of the regulator handle.

The surface of the main valve on its trunk-like extension is developed in a series of graduated slits, or steam-passages, which are provided to ensure a gradual admission.

It is claimed that a regulator of this form conduces to perfect control by the driver, and enables him to instantaneously shut off steam if the driving wheels stop.

A form much used with superheated engines is illustrated in the next chapter.

Lagging.

The external surfaces of the boiler and outer fire-box exposed to the atmosphere are covered with non-conducting material, or " lagged," to conserve as much as possible the heat within, and prevent loss by radiation. Originally wood was used, applied in strips round the boiler barrel, bound together with bands and covered over with the steel sheeting which forms the finish. This wood lagging has now been almost entirely superseded by prepared mattresses of asbestos, felt, etc., or by plastic compounds of magnesia, silica, etc., applied as blocks or in semi-liquid form; slag wool and glass silk are also used.

Fig. 28 illustrates the boiler of a modern express locomotive coated with lagging-mattresses being lifted into the under-frame ready for the final covering of cleading-sheets of planished steel.

Some of the plastic compounds are applied when the boiler is heated. Many of the mattresses are held away from the boiler on " pegs," or " stools," which preserve an air space between the boiler plate and the mattress, it having been found that any moisture from condensation or leakage impregnating the mattress causes local corrosion of the plates if the latter are allowed to be in contact. Whatever non-conducting substance is used it is eventually covered with steel clothing plates securely held round the boiler by bands.

There is a tendency now to use the compounds in block form of suitable size and thickness which can be easily cut and shaped to enable a close covering to be made.

As regards the non-conductivity of the various compounds, it is

By courtesy of J. W. Roberts, Ltd., Armley.

FIG. 28.—LAGGING A LOCOMOTIVE BOILER.

claimed that with asbestos mattress of approved manufacture and having suitable air spaces comprised in it, a saving is effected of about 90 per cent. in the loss of heat which would otherwise take place from the unprotected boiler plates.

Removable Coverings.

Among those in use for lagging locomotive boilers the chief are asbestos mattresses consisting of outer sheets of asbestos cloth in which prepared asbestos fibre is filled. The asbestos cloth should be of good and pure quality or it will deteriorate when heated, and most users specify that the loss of heat is kept strictly within reasonable limits.

The asbestos cloth is so sewn together and stitched at intervals with metallic asbestos yarn that the enclosed fibre cannot shift. In another form the asbestos is used in the form of felt in place of fibre. Mattresses made in this manner are considered stronger and more lasting; both forms can be easily fitted to the boiler and easily removed or replaced.

An improvement in the manufacture of these mattresses consists in fitting them with " stools " by which they are supported on the boiler-plates, thus providing an air-space between them and the asbestos clothing. This air-space adds to the efficiency in heat conservation and also has the advantage of preventing the mattresses sticking to the boiler-plates should there be any escape of steam or water from defective joints or rivets. These " stools " are usually of metal but are also made of compressed asbestos.

Another application of aluminium for this purpose consists of providing the metal in the form of foil and then making a mattress of it from a number of sheets assembled together as a mass in which air is imprisoned.

Glass Silk as Lagging.

A new product for the heat insulation of steam boilers, pipes, tanks, ducts, etc., which has already found considerable application in marine engineering is known as glass silk. It is now being used for the insulation of locomotive boilers.

As its name suggests, glass silk is composed of very fine threads of spun glass, which closely resemble silk in appearance. The threads possess a surprisingly high tensile strength, and when spread into the various forms suitable for heat insulation, produce a network of fibres highly resistant to vibratory influences, which is such an important consideration in railway engineering practice.

While " still " air is an almost perfect heat insulator, it is not possible in practice to take advantage of the solution which the apparent simplicity of this fact may suggest. Means must be found to imprison the air in such a manner that, under changing temperature conditions, it will remain stationary for all practical purposes.

As regards " diatomaceous " earths, and other similar porous substances, advantage is taken of the minute air-cells which constitute the pores in their structure, and in order to bind the materials together for the purpose of practical application, fibrous substances are added. This introduction of extraneous matter, which in itself possesses relatively low powers of resistance to heat flow, detracts considerably from the efficiency of the whole.

It is claimed that glass silk with its long, fine, silken fibre offers a very practical solution of the problem. The air-cells are imprisoned between the threads which when spread into the various forms lie closely together, and since they can be stretched and possess a natural tendency to cling together in network formation, the addition of binding materials is quite unnecessary.

Glass silk is quite incombustible, and is guaranteed to withstand temperatures as high as 900° F. In fact, it has been tested and proved up to a temperature as high as 1100° F. Being glass it is rot-proof and offers no sustenance to vermin; further, it neither causes corrosion nor is attacked by any chemical with the exception of hydrofluoric acid.

CHAPTER III

Superheating.

STEAM generated in a boiler is in contact with the water and is known as " saturated steam," as it is necessarily more or less laden with moisture. The ordinary non-superheater locomotive makes use of such saturated steam in its original condition, as generated, except for such slight drying as occurs when the steam is passing from the regulator through the steam-pipes in the smoke-box, to the cylinders.

As is well known, water boils in an open vessel, at sea-level, at a temperature of 212° F. (100° C.), but if the vessel is closed and heat still supplied, steam will be generated creating pressure on the surface of the liquid inside the vessel. This will cause an increase in the temperature required to boil the water, so that there is a rising temperature as the pressure increases (as shown in Fig. 1) the temperature curve for the gradual increase of pressure in saturated steam. Adding heat to the water, and to the steam in contact with the water, more water will be evaporated and the quantity of steam increased, the saturation temperature increasing with the pressure.

From this it will be seen that if the temperature be lowered at any point in the curve shown in Fig. 1, by allowing the steam to come into contact with the surfaces of cooler pipes, cylinders, etc., the pressure will also fall, as the steam will be immediately condensed and form water. If extra heat is added to the steam at any point in the curve, this will either cause the pressure to rise or steam to dry, so that its temperature is above that actually due to pressure; in other words, it will become " superheated."

It is thus understood that superheated steam may undergo cooling to the amount of the added temperature without condensation taking place. On Fig. 1 a second curve will be noticed, marked " vol. curve." This represents the volume of saturated steam per unit of weight (say, cubic foot per lb.) diminishing with each increase of temperature and pressure.

Superheated steam possesses the valuable property of increasing its volume with increase of temperature. The moisture in the saturated steam being turned into more steam, so that if the steam space is restricted or closed—or, say, the volume kept constant, the pressure will rise according to the temperature. With pistons moving to and fro there is continually expanding space, therefore, any extra heat applied to the steam by passing it through the superheater pipes raises the temperature and increases its volume, whilst the pressure remains the same as that in the boiler; this point is illustrated in Fig. 2.

The curve shows the volume of superheated steam at 175 lbs. per sq. in., absolute (160 lbs. per sq. in. by the pressure gauge) for different

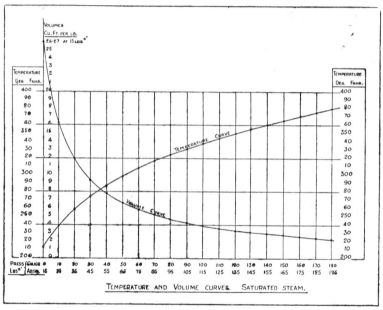

FIG. 1.

amounts of superheat. Such steam in its saturated state has a temperature of 370·8° F., and a volume of 2·6 cubic ft. per lb. If this steam is passed through the superheater so as to add 100° F. to its temperature its volume is increased to 3·04 cubic ft. per lb., or 17 per cent. increase, whilst if 200° F. are added the volume will be increased to 3·44 cubic ft. per lb., or an increase of 32 per cent. This is graphically shown by the comparative spheres given in Fig. 3.

From the foregoing it will be seen that the increase in volume enables more work to be obtained from saturated steam generated in the boiler if extra heat is added to it after it has left the boiler, by passing it through a superheater on its way to the cylinders; thus the steam-producing ability of a boiler will be increased without having to provide increased heating surface and grate area, as would be the case if a larger boiler were installed.

From what has been noted it will be clear that superheating will tend to make the steam more " gaseous," as the addition of heat has converted the moisture pre-existing in the steam into " gas," which is

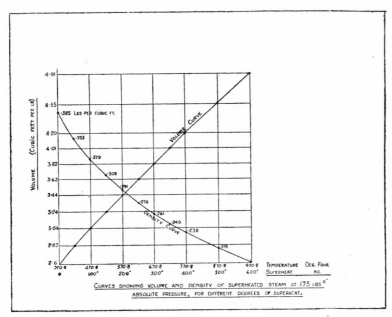

FIG. 2.

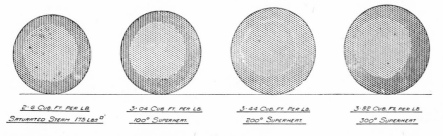

FIG. 3.

far more fluid and ready to pass the surfaces of the steam-pipes with reduced friction, permitting higher velocity when passing through, with the advantage that it carries away the heat more rapidly; and, incidentally, the steam-pipes conveying the steam to the cylinders may be of less diameter than when required for saturated steam.

It will now be understood that superheated steam coming into contact with the surfaces of the steam-chest, cylinders, etc., may lose heat to the extent of the amount which has been added without condensation taking place, exactly the reverse of what occurs with saturated steam.

General Results of Superheating.

It is claimed that with the moderate superheat secured by the use of apparatus utilizing the heat from the waste gases in the smoke-box there must be economy effected, as otherwise this heat would be entirely lost. Although, on the other hand, it may be urged that if the steam had been efficiently generated in the boiler, the remaining products of combustion would reach the smoke-box at such a comparatively low temperature that not much benefit could be gained. However, be this as it may, with the usual superheating arrangements there is no diversion of heat produced in the furnace from its original purpose of generating steam; the superheating obtained is entirely additional. If, however, attempts are made at securing very high superheat, then it may be necessary to divert some of the fire-box heat from original steam generation.

The latter would appear to be a powerful argument against attempting very high superheat, as more heat units would have to be produced in the furnace, or the boiler efficiency reduced. This is not really so, for although some of the heat units may be diverted from steam generation to superheating, a much smaller quantity of steam requires to be raised in the boiler. Indeed, after a smaller amount of steam has been produced and the further heat utilized to superheat this quantity of steam, the total number of heat units absorbed may be appreciably less than those required for getting the same power output with either saturated or moderately superheated steam. The advocates of high superheat also carry this argument a step further by pointing out that it is quite possible to use in conjunction with a high degree superheater a boiler that is actually smaller and yet does the same work, whereas moderate super-heat will not offer the same possibilities. It may be suggested here that under some circumstances a feed-water heater may constitute a more suitable means of utilizing some of the waste heat.

The smaller boiler policy has not been adopted in general practice, although many instances can be found which somewhat suggest it. It has been found that by fitting a high-temperature superheater, an engine of somewhat smaller standard design can be perpetuated to do the work, otherwise a larger locomotive would have to be provided to meet increased traffic requirements. Although retaining the same size of boiler as before, the weight of steam required may be reduced, so that there is sufficient heat not only for steam generation (with a reduced heating surface) but for superheating in addition, without impairing the steam efficiency of the boiler; further, as the steam demand is less, it may be that the generation is rendered more efficient.

By way of further convincing, the diagram Fig. 3A is given, wherein the claims set forth for the benefits derived from superheating are pictorially represented.

Naturally, there are some properties which must be taken into

(1) *Saturated Steam Locomotive.*
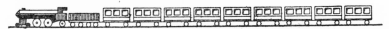

2) *Locomotive using Moderate Superheat (50°-100° F.),*

3) *Superheated Steam Locomotive using high Superheat more than 200° F.).*

(*a*) COMPARISON OF COAL AND WATER CONSUMPTION OF SATURATED AND SUPERHEATED STEAM LOCOMOTIVES FOR THE SAME TRACTIVE EFFORT.

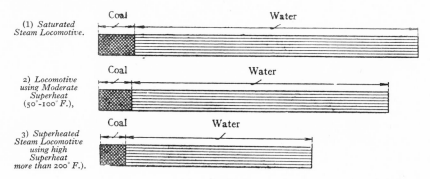

(1) Saturated Steam Locomotive.

(2) Locomotive using Moderate Superheat (50–100° F.).

(3) Superheated Steam Locomotive using high Superheat (more than 200° F.).

(*b*) COMPARISON OF THE HAULAGE POWER OF SATURATED AND SUPERHEATED STEAM LOCOMOTIVES FOR THE SAME AMOUNT OF COAL BURNT IN ENGINES OF THE SAME WEIGHT.

FIG. 3A.

consideration when using superheated steam in the engine. Its action is somewhat rough on details it comes into contact with, owing to its dry, hot, scouring nature, and entire lack of moisture, thus possessing no lubricating properties. This needs special attention in regard to good lubrication of moving parts in contact with superheated steam. Soft metals, such as white metal, brass, copper, etc., cannot be used in contact with superheated steam, as they are scored by it, much as though they had been subjected to a sand-blast. Harder and tougher materials, such as wrought or cast-iron, steel, etc., must be used for valves, pistons, guides, bushes, etc.

The main principles upon which the production and use of super-heated steam is based having been described, the apparatus for obtaining these results will next be explained.

The coloured diagram (Fig. 4) gives in a concise manner the arrangement of a superheater as applied to a modern locomotive. It should be noted that there are many modifications of the details, such as the joining up of the elements, their arrangement in the "header," or in the disposition of the element tubes in the smoke-box. The diagram will, however, be sufficient for explanatory purposes, the colours denoting where saturated steam becomes superheated steam. On perusal it will be noticed that the heating surface of the boiler is divided into two distinct portions, one consisting of the fire-box, with small smoke-tubes " G " and the large flue-tubes " F " generating the saturated steam, as usual, whilst the second portion consists of superheating elements " E," located inside the large flues " F," providing the extra heating surface by which the saturated steam becomes superheated.

FIG. 5.—PROGRESSIVE STAGES IN THE MANUFACTURE OF "M.L.S." SOLID MACHINE-FORGED RETURN BENDS.

Elements.

The "elements" used for the superheater have been the subject of much study and experiment. To secure reliable tubes to withstand the high temperature and pressure has required profound consideration on the part of manufacturers. Fig. 5 shows the steps taken in the making of steel elements from cold-drawn steel tubing forged at the bend; two lengths of tubing are welded together in a machine to form the return bend, as shown.

In operation saturated steam from the surfaces of the water in the boiler is collected in the steam space above the fire-box, and passes down the collector pipe " A " to the regulator " C," which is arranged in casting " D," having two chambers, the rear one being connected up to the pipes or elements for saturated steam, and the front for the reception of the return after superheating. Each of these superheater tubes or elements leads from the "header" down the large flue-tube to within a short distance of the fire-box, terminating in a hollow

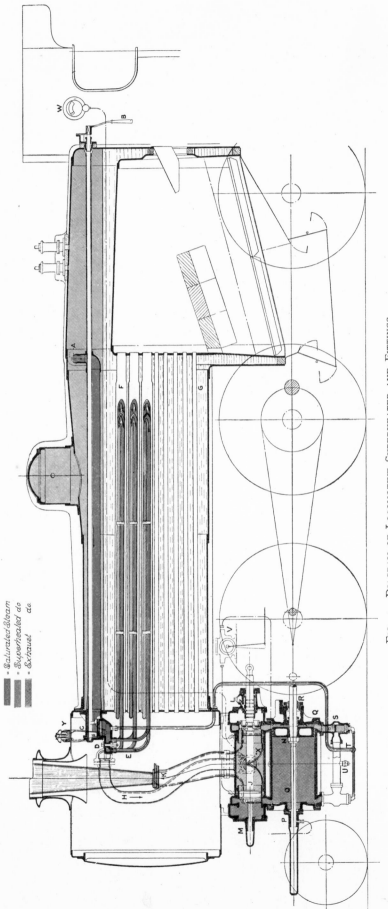

FIG. 4.—DIAGRAM OF LOCOMOTIVE SUPERHEATER AND FITTINGS.

REFERENCES.

A STEAM COLLECTOR PIPE.
B REGULATOR HANDLE.
C REGULATOR IN SMOKE-BOX.
D STEAM COLLECTOR OR HEADER.
E ELEMENTS.
F LARGE FLUE-TUBES CONTAINING ELEMENTS.
G SMALL SMOKE-TUBES.
H STEAM-PIPES.
J PISTON VALVE AND SPINDLE.
K BLAST-PIPE.
L REAR STEAM-CHEST COVER, GUIDE AND GLAND.
M FRONT STEAM-CHEST COVER AND GUIDE.

N PISTON AND ROD.
O PISTON-ROD TAIL ROD.
P PISTON-ROD TAIL GUIDE IN FRONT CYLINDER COVER.
Q HIND CYLINDER COVER.
R AIR-COOLED METALLIC PACKING FOR PISTON-ROD.
S CYLINDER RELIEF VALVE AND BY-PASS (AUTOMATIC).
T STEAM-PIPE TO BY-PASS.
U DRAIN TO BY-PASS PIPE.
V MECHANICAL LUBRICATOR.
W PYROMETER IN CAB.
X PYROMETER BULB IN STEAM-PIPE.
Y VACUUM RELIEF VALVE ON HEADER.

= Saturated Steam
= Superheated do
= Exhaust do

[*To face page* 50

" arrow " head, from which the return tube passes back through the flue to the front chamber " E." In effect this means that the steam has traversed between 30 and 40 ft. of " element " subject to the hot gases from the fire-box, ensuring its return to the header in a super-heated state, with a gain of, probably, 250° F., whence it passes to the steam-pipe for use in the steam-chest and cylinders.

Headers.

The " Maunsell " header, used in the Southern Railway locomotive, " Lord Nelson," is illustrated in detail in Fig. 6. In this the saturated

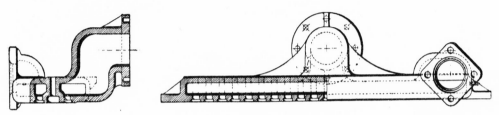

FIG. 6.—" M.L.S." MAUNSELL HEADER, TYPE AC.

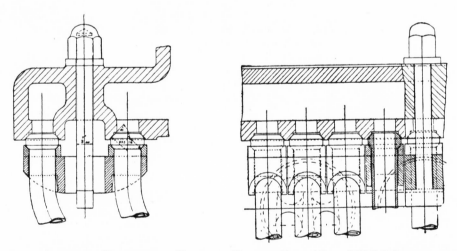

FIG. 7.—ATTACHING ELEMENTS TO MAUNSELL HEADER, TYPE AC. " M.L.S." SUPERHEATER.

and superheated steam-chambers extend right across the header, the dividing partition being enlarged at intervals to permit of openings being made to allow the attaching bolts to pass through, as shown. The enlarged sketch, Fig. 7, also gives details of the ball-joints, used to secure steam-tight connections. The connecting bolts are formed with " T " heads, adapted to pass through elongated slots in the flanges, and then turned through a right angle, so as to fit in hollow grooves provided to retain them; secure engagement is thus obtained. To remove an element the nut is slackened and the bolt turned and drawn through the slot in the flange into a recess in the base of the header, after which the element can be readily withdrawn. Centrally, the rear compartment of the header is enlarged to receive the main steam-pipe from the regulator, whilst the ends of the front compartment are formed to receive the steam-pipe connections to the cylinders.

The reason why so many elements are provided (usually twenty or more) is that steam has a somewhat low thermal conductivity. It does not take up heat readily, therefore it is necessary to divide the boiler steam into a number of thin streams so that all the particles are enabled to take up heat from the flue gases.

Piston Valves.

For the employment of superheated steam, the cylinders of the locomotive are provided with special piston valves " J " suitable for use with highly heated steam. In those shown the steam is distributed from the inside edges of the valve heads, thus keeping the superheated steam from exposure to cooler influences outside and also dispensing with the need for any valve spindle packing to be directly in contact.

The body of the valve head is in two portions, between which are fitted steam and exhaust rings, which by the effect of the steam pressure on the inside diaphragm of each head close tightly there, preventing the rings from being forced against the liner by the full pressure of the steam on the inside. This avoids undue wear of the bridges at the port and also excessive compression tending to collapse the rings inwards.

The joints in the rings are arranged to go over a wide bridge on the liner, a condition which should be carefully observed. This valve is known as the " Schmidt " type.

Cylinders.

With " inside " admission, as shown, the exhaust takes place on the outside of each valve head, chambers being provided in the cylinder casting at each end. These are joined together through the passage connecting with the blast-pipe " K." In this case the weight of the valve and spindle " J " is carried by a tail-rod in a bush in the front steam-chest cover " M."

An enlarged drawing of a cylinder, with its piston valve, glands, bye-pass, and water release valves, together with a relief valve, is shown in Fig. 8. The packings, or main piston and valve spindles, are of the metallic, air-cooled type, where the white metal, or bronze, rings are well removed from the effects of the highly heated steam. Enclosed in a case surrounded by a cavity open to the atmosphere the packings can adjust themselves to the alignments of the rods through the coiled spring. The water release valves are still more important details, as when an engine has been standing for any length of time with regulator closed, the water may accumulate in the long superheater pipes and find its way to the steam-chest and cylinders. Steam-valves of this description must, therefore, be provided.

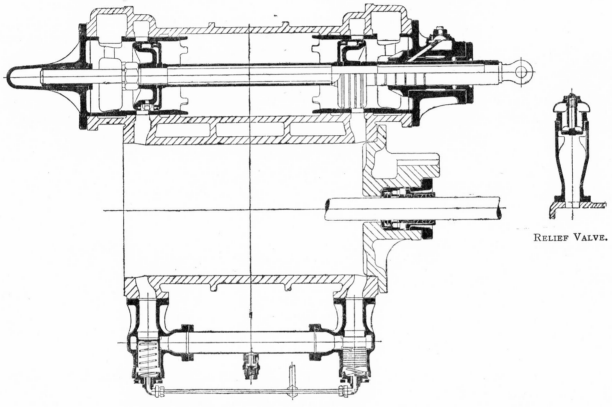

RELIEF VALVE.

FIG. 8.—PISTON VALVE AND GLANDS, BYE-PASS AND WATER RELEASE VALVES AND RELIEF VALVE ON HEADER.

Relief Valves.

Superheater locomotives are usually fitted with some form of relief valves (Fig. 8) set on the collector. The function of this valve is to counteract the effect on the steam-chest and pipes of the pumping action of the moving pistons, being placed on the superheater side of the regulator. When this latter is closed and no steam circulates through the superheater tubes, air drawn in through relief valves assists in keeping the elements cool, and thus avoids the risk of burning these important details.

Regulator for Superheater.

In the locomotive given in the frontispiece the regulator is placed at the extreme end of the steam-pipe in the dome, which, consequently, controls the steam before it enters the superheater. When steam is shut off, the tubes of these will be left empty and liable to overheating, especially if the superheater has been designed for a high degree of superheat.

A modification of the superheater arrangement places the regulator in such a position that it controls the steam *after* it has circulated through the elements; or, in other words, it is placed on the superheater side— being located in the smoke-box; this practice has been largely adopted,

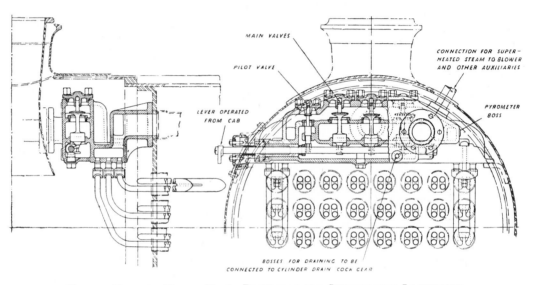

FIG. 9.—MULTIPLE POPPET VALVE REGULATOR FOR SUPERHEATED LOCOMOTIVE.

and much can be said in its favour. The regulator being exposed to very high temperatures, it has been deemed expedient to design a special multiple valve arrangement wherein a number of small circular, double-beat valves are fitted in the header, and are operated by a cross-shaft turned by the lever in the cab. Figs. 9 and 10 illustrate this.

The casing carrying the valves is cast with the header, and consists of three chambers, one above the other, in the front of this. The upper chamber forms part of the superheated steam compartment, and has a flange connection at one end from which a steam supply is taken to the auxiliaries. The middle chamber is in direct communication with the main steam-pipe, and the third, or bottom chamber is occupied by the balancing piston, the three together housing the regulator valves. These valves consist of a number—varying according to the size of the boiler—

of relatively small, circular single-seated, steel valves operated by a cam-shaft extending through the lower chamber, and connected on the exterior of this, to the regulator-rod. The stem of each main valve carries a balancing piston at the bottom, and a disc-like throttle valve at the top. The balancing is effected through the medium of a small pilot valve placed at the extreme end of the valve casing, which valve on the first movement of the regular handle lifts and admits steam to the lower chamber, and therefore below the balancing pistons of the main valves. Further movement of the handle with the cam-shaft causes the first of the main valves to open, then raises the valve at the opposite end of the casing; this is followed by lifting the centre valve, or if there are four main valves the one coming between the centre valve and that at the other end. On lifting the first main valve a small quantity of steam will pass from the upper to the central chamber, and the successive opening of the remaining valves provides a perfect graduation of the steam supply to the cylinders of the engine. All is so nearly balanced that the regulator handle requires the smallest degree of effort on the part of the driver to control it.

Closing of the valves takes place in the reverse order—that which opened last being the first to close, and the others following successively in the order in which they opened, a pilot closing the last. This operation is accomplished partly by the mechanical action of the cams and partly by the weight of each valve plus the pressure of steam on the top, due to its area being slightly greater than that of the balancing piston. The regulator handle has a pull-and-push movement transmitted by a bell-crank on the cam-shaft lever at the smoke-box, by a rod carried through the handrail and attached to either end of the compensating lever, which neutralizes any effect of contraction and expansion of the boiler.

It is claimed for this device that the provision of dampers, draught retarders, steam-circulating valve, and other accessories to afford protection to the superheater elements are unnecessary. As the superheater tubes are continually under pressure, superheater steam is available for all auxiliaries—feed-pumps, brake apparatus, etc.; the effective steam space of the boiler is increased, and there results a reduction in priming, with more effective control of the engine, owing to the very small steam space between the regulator and cylinders. Further, easier maintenance of steam-tight valves is claimed.

Pyrometers.

Although it is not usually considered necessary to fit a pyrometer to a superheater locomotive, still, such an instrument is useful for providing constant and reliable indication of the engine's performance. If the firing is not being satisfactorily done, if the water is too high in the boiler, if the tubes are becoming foul, or if the general working of the engine is not as it should be there will be a drop in the steam temperature, and this will be shown at once by the pyrometer.

There are many types of pyrometers in use. A satisfactory one consists of three parts: (1) a steam fixture (containing the hot junction of the thermo-couple), which screws into the steam-pipe, or steam-chest, of the engine; (2) an indicator to be placed in the cab; and (3) the coupling connecting the fixture to the indicator. The cold junction of the thermo-couple is at atmospheric temperature, and variations in the temperature are automatically compensated; the hot junction of the thermo-couple is directly exposed to the flow of super-heated steam, and the variations in the steam temperature immediately affect the current gener-

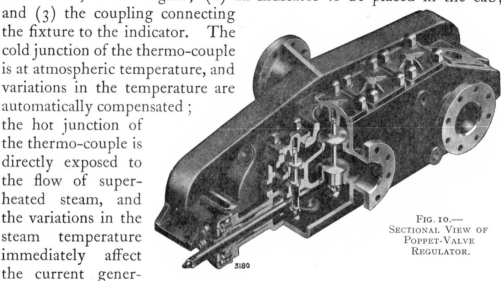

Fig. 10.—
Sectional View of
Poppet-Valve
Regulator.

ated, and show the change instantaneously upon the dial in the cab.

Pyrometers are more often fitted on locomotives of the continental railways than on those of this country.

Lubrication for Superheated Locomotives.

The lubrication of cylinders, valves, etc., is another important matter with superheaters, a primary essential being that the lubricant used must be capable of withstanding temperatures up to 650° F. without deterioration of any of its lubricating properties. Heavy mineral oils are generally used with flash point above 550° F., and to ensure this getting to the surfaces required, side-feed displacement lubricators, or mechanical force-feed devices, are used. These arrangements will be referred to later, but the approved points for inducting lubrication on both outside and inside cylindered superheater locomotives are shown in Figs. 11 and 12.

No matter what system of lubrication is used, or what grade of oil, there is sure to be a certain amount of carbonization, or accumulation of hard matter on the surfaces of the valves, pistons, port-bridges, etc.

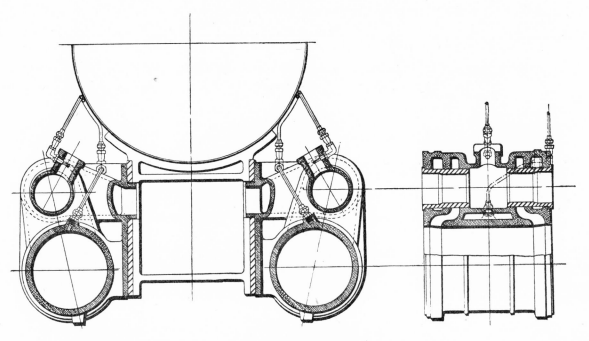

FIG. 11.—OIL INDUCT ARRANGEMENT FOR OUTSIDE CYLINDER LOCOMOTIVE.

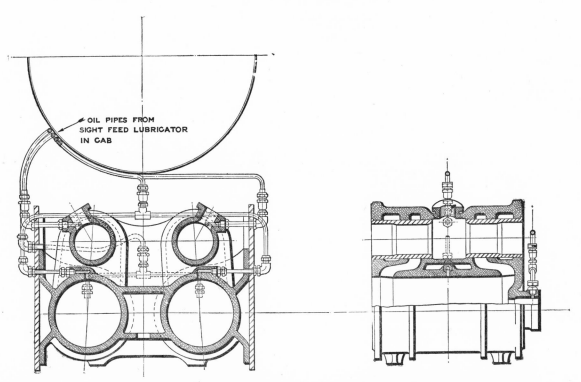

OIL PIPES FROM
SIGHT FEED LUBRICATOR
IN CAB

FIG. 12.—OIL INDUCT ARRANGEMENT FOR INSIDE CYLINDER LOCOMOTIVE.

This, if allowed to accumulate, will cause excessive wear of valve rings, liners, etc., and also choke any lubricating grooves and oil-holes. These remarks are not altogether confined to superheated engines; the trouble exists, in a minor degree, in those using saturated steam, but with the higher temperatures of the former there is a greater tendency for its formation. The obvious remedy is either to prevent the smoke-box gases and deposits from being drawn through the blast-pipe, or attempt to neutralize the effect by some automatic, or special, device. The steam-chest relief valve already described is one remedy; another is to neutralize the effect on gases being drawn in by allowing the engine a little steam at the regulator, when this is closed and the engine "coasting." Such action will dilute the impurities drawn from the smoke-box, and so reduce their tendency to deposit on the surfaces; further, the oil will not carbonize on the surfaces so readily in the presence of steam. This explains why some makers of mechanical lubricators provide an anti-carbonizing device in connection with their devices, wherein a jet of steam is arranged so that it can mix with the oil to form an emulsion in the cylinders; such an emulsion provides the oily atmosphere required for the pistons, valves, etc., to work under special conditions.

Other Devices for Superheater Locomotives.

Whilst it is desirable to use piston valves for highly superheated steam, it is not actually imperative to do so, and many engines with

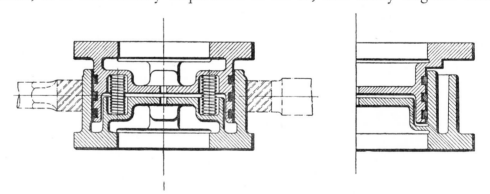

FIG. 13.—BALANCED SLIDE-VALVE FOR SUPERHEATER LOCOMOTIVES.

ordinary slide valves have been converted from saturated steam practice by substituting a modified balanced slide valve. A suitable design for such a detail is shown in Fig. 13, which is said to have proved very successful in use.

CHAPTER IV

Cylinders—Valves and Valve Gears—Stephenson's, Gooch's, Walschaert's—Motion Details—
Coupling Rods—Woodward Drive—Roller Bearings.

Cylinders.

NEXT to the boiler, in which steam is generated, the more important details of a steam locomotive are the cylinders and motion, these being the means by which the energy of the steam is transformed into useful work—namely, propulsion of the engine, with its load. Primarily, the engine consists of cylinders into which the steam is admitted to move the pistons, whose reciprocating motion is transformed through the medium of cranks to a rotary one of the wheels, thus propelling the engine either backwards or forwards, as desired.

Valve Motion.

To operate the valves distributing the steam supply to the cylinders, a " motion " is required which will cause the valves to be moved as to admit steam alternately to either side of the pistons, and allow that on the opposite side (which has done its work) to discharge through the blast-pipe to the atmosphere. In the case of a locomotive, it is absolutely essential that this motion should be reversible, to allow the engine to travel in either direction.

Position of Cylinders.

The cylinders are usually located at the front of the engine, either between the frames, for an " inside " cylinder, or on the outside for what is termed an " outside " cylinder engine. The diagram, Fig. 1, shows the more common arrangement of cylinders: the valves may be either slide or piston. " A " represents a pair of cylinders with the valves above, below, or between them. " B " similarly gives piston valves located above or below; " C " and " D " give outside cylinders, with the slide or piston valves in their more ordinary positions. " E," " F," and " G " give arrangements where three cylinders are employed, whilst " H " has the ordinary position for piston valves with four cylinders. (The shaded outlines give the alternative positions.)

The cranks may be arranged either with the right-hand or left-hand crank leading; the difference will be noted in the diagrams " J "

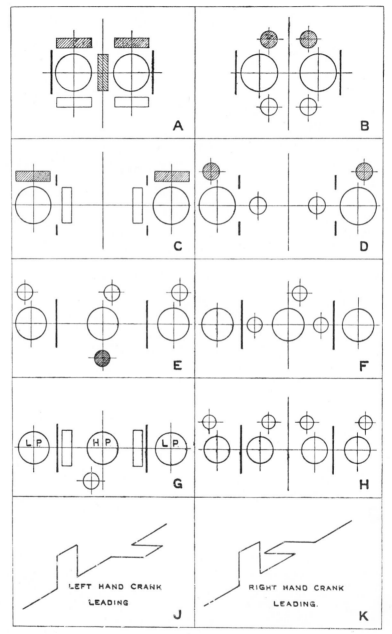

FIG. 1—POSITIONS OF CYLINDERS AND CRANKS.

and " K." This relationship in the cranks to each other, as to which leads, has nothing to do with the running of the engine; it only concerns the design, inasmuch that all crank-pins for coupling rods, etc., must be made to correspond with the procedure adopted.

Compound Locomotives.

Compound locomotives, in which the expansion of the boiler steam is partially carried out in one cylinder and completed in another, or more, are favoured in many countries, and are also in service here. These locomotives may have two, three, or four cylinders. If only two, then one will receive boiler steam, and is known as the H.P. (high pressure), whilst the other, taking the exhaust steam from the first, is the L.P. (low pressure). In a four-cylinder compound locomotive there are usually two H.P. and two L.P. cylinders.

The locomotive illustrated in our frontispiece has four cylinders, all H.P., with piston valves as now largely adopted, supplanting the earlier D. valves. Piston valves (as their name implies) are of circular form, in which ports are arranged circumferentially.

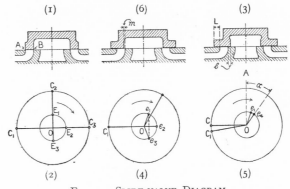

FIG. 2.—SLIDE-VALVE DIAGRAM.

Slide-valves.

The original form of slide-valve, known as the " D " valve, consists of a flat, box-shaped casting which, when actuated by the eccentrics, can slide over the steam ports of the cylinder so that each is uncovered in turn to receive the steam, whilst the other is put into communication with the exhaust through the cavity cast in the valve. A reference to the accompanying Fig. 2 will explain this. At (1) the valve is shown in mid-position just covering the ports, the diagram being to such proportions that if the valve is moved from the position shown to the right then the left-hand port will open to steam at " A," but as there is no " lap " shown there is no provision for " cutting-off " the steam before the piston has completed its stroke, and thus providing for any further expansion of the steam. Since the steam port has been open during the whole stroke of the piston, high-pressure boiler steam has been following it throughout, so that as the exhaust opens, the cylinder full of high-pressure steam will be able to escape without hindrance or delay.

In (2) the eccentric is in the position OE/2, and the crank has moved from OC/1 to OC/2. The return stroke of the valve then begins, and when the eccentric has reached OE/3, and the crank is at OC/3, the left-hand outside edge " A " of the valve has just closed and the exhaust edge " B " is beginning to open the steam-port to exhaust. The crank, during this movement of the valve, has made a half revolution from C/1 to C/3, and the piston has moved through one stroke of its travel.

In (3) the conditions have been modified, and the valve made wider to overlap the ports by the amount " L," so that before the left-hand edge of the valve can uncover the left-hand port to admit steam, it must move towards the right by an amount equal to " L."

Referring to (4), with the crank at OC/1 and the piston at the end of its stroke, the eccentric will now be in the position Oe/1, when the left-hand port just begins to open; therefore, the addition of the lap " L " has necessitated the eccentric being moved on the crankshaft, or " advanced " through the angle AOe/1, as shown in (5). The longer the outside lap, the larger will be this angle.

The effect of this outside lap is to cause the valve to close the port before the piston has completed its stroke. The steam is thus " cut off " and imprisoned in the cylinder for a period before the exhaust commences, doing more useful work on the piston. In (4) the cut-off is shown as accomplished before the end of the piston stroke. Suppose the piston to be at C/1, with the crank on left-hand " dead-centre " OC/1, the position of the eccentric, as previously explained, will be at Oe/1, and the left-hand port is just on the point of being opened to admit steam. When the centre of the eccentric, revolving in the direction of the arrow, has reached e/2, the valve is at the extreme right hand of its travel, and commencing to return. When the centre of the eccentric has arrived at e/3, the left-hand edge of the outside lap of the valve will have returned to the position which it occupied when the eccentric was at e/1; and since the port was just being opened when the eccentric was at e/1, it will now be at the point of closing with the eccentric at 2/3, the valve being moved in the opposite direction. From the time of opening to that of closing the port, the eccentric has moved through the angle e/1 Oe/3. The crank must, therefore, have moved from OC/1 through the equal angle which determines its new position, when steam is cut off. This shows that the piston has travelled through about three-quarters of its stroke.

By increasing the amount " L," or steam lap, for a given length of valve travel, the point of cut-off is made earlier. The travel is equal to twice the amount—maximum port opening plus steam lap; this latter is generally about 1 in., but may be more, necessitating longer valve travel.

So far it has been assumed in (4) that when the edge of the valve is beginning to open the port to steam, the piston is at the extreme end of its stroke, with the crank on the dead-centre, OC/1. It is usual, however, to admit steam to the cylinder just *before* the piston starts its stroke, thus providing a cushion for bringing the piston and the reciprocating parts to rest at the dead-point, without shock, as their motion reverses. This is termed " lead," and should amount to about an eighth of an inch in the usual running position of the valve-gear. With the Stephenson link motion, this lead varies in different positions of the reversing lever.

The relative positions OC/1 and Oe/1 of the crank and eccentric, when the valve has outside lap but no lead, are also shown at (4). In (5) Oe/1 represents this position of the eccentric, and if, when the crank is on dead-centre at OC, the left-hand port is to be opened by the amount of the lead, the valve must be moved still more towards the right. This involves a further shifting of the eccentric round the axle from e/1 to a new position, e/4. Oe/4 is the position of the eccentric when the crank is at OC, and in this position the port is opened to steam by the amount of the lead. When the port is on the point of opening, the eccentric is at Oe/1, but the crank is at Oc/1, and the piston has not completed its stroke from right to left. The total angle " a " of advance of the eccentric is AOe/4, and may be taken as the sum of two angles, viz.: AOe/1, due to the lap of the valve and e/1 Oe/4, due to the lead.

At (1), Fig. 2, the inside edge " B " of the valve is in mid-position, but at (3) the inside edge of the valve overlaps the inside edge of the port by the amount " l," which is known as the " inside," or exhaust lap. If the left-hand port be due to open to exhaust, it is obvious that the exhaust edge " B " of the valve will uncover the port in (1) before the similar edge in (3) will do so. The effect of the inside, or exhaust, lap is to delay the exhaust, thus prolonging the period of expansion; but when the valve is moving in the opposite direction, from left to right, the exhaust edge at (3) will close the exhaust sooner than would be the case as at (1). The result has the effect of causing compression of the steam towards the end of the stroke. Inside lap is seldom used owing to the fear of causing excessive compression. The latter may be produced when there is no positive exhaust or inside lap, as (1). In this case, the release of steam is expedited, and the port kept open longer to exhaust by cutting away the inner edge of the port, as in (6). The amount m is the " inside clearance," or negative exhaust lap. This procedure is adopted to reduce the back pressure on the pistons, and the amount of the inside clearance, when given, is usually very small—about 1/32nd of an inch.

The form of " D " slide-valve which has been referred to is given

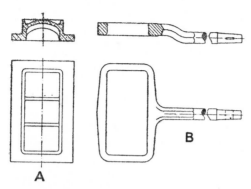

FIG. 3.—SLIDE-VALVE AND BUCKLE.

in Fig. 3. In this the valve " A," of bronze, is embraced by a buckle " B," formed in one piece, with the valve spindle. The bent spindle is particularly applicable to loco- motives having their steam-chest and valves between the cylinders (see A in Fig. 1), in order to provide sufficient space for the stuffing-boxes. With valves above or below the cylinders, no such " off-set " is required.

Valve Movements.

Fig. 4 shows the cycle of valve movements. In " L " the piston is at the extreme end of its stroke, and is about to move from left to right. The valve, it will be noticed, is moving in the same direction, and has just opened the left-hand port for the admission of steam by what is termed " amount of lead." At " M " the piston has reached a position approaching half-stroke, and the valve has made its extreme movement to the right, and is about to reverse. The left-hand port is now fully

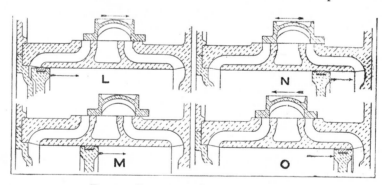

FIG. 4.—DIAGRAM OF VALVE MOVEMENTS.

open to steam. In the next position, " N," the valve is moving to the left, and has reached the position when its left-hand edge has just closed the port. At O the valve is still moving towards the left, and the piston has reached the end of its stroke. The valve has commenced to uncover the left port to exhaust (known as the " point of release "), thence the steam will escape through the cavity inside the valve, through the exhaust port of the cylinders to the blast-pipe. The piston, moving in the opposite direction, is propelled by steam entering the opposite end of the cylinder in precisely the same manner as already outlined.

A modified form of " D " slide-valve, which has been largely used, is known as the " trick " valve, Fig. 5, whereby an additional steam passage is provided for steam entering the cylinder, this ensuring a larger port opening to steam for a small movement of the valve, diminishing the tendency to " wire-draw " steam when the engine is running at high speed. For a movement of, say, $\frac{1}{8}$ in. to the right from the point of admission, the left port is uncovered $\frac{1}{8}$ in. by the left-hand edge of the valve.

FIG. 5.—TRICK VALVE.

The internal passage to the steam-port is also opened an $\frac{1}{8}$ in. at the right hand, and consequently a total equivalent of $\frac{1}{8}$ in. $+ \frac{1}{8}$ in. $= \frac{1}{4}$ in. is given for a valve movement of only $\frac{1}{8}$ in.

Balanced Slide-valves.

Balanced valves, in which the back of the slide-valve is relieved of pressure, have also been much used. A section of such a valve is shown at " D," Fig. 6, where a " pressure " plate is bolted to the inside of the steam-chest cover. The back of the slide-valve is made steam-tight by the grooves seen at " E," filled with flat, rectangular strips, held up by

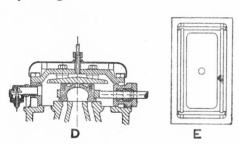

D   E

FIG. 6.—BALANCED VALVE.

springs. By this means pressure above the valve is relieved, and the slide-valve moves between the two surfaces with much less friction. In the crown of the valve a hole is provided, so that should any leakage of boiler steam pass the strips, it will escape into the exhaust cavity of the valve. An inward opening valve will be also noticed on the steam-chest, to admit air when the engine is running without steam.

In the construction described a certain area of the back of the valve is enclosed within the frame formed by the strips, so that this area is relieved from the high steam pressure in the steam-chest, and is subject only to the pressure of the exhaust. That part of the back of the valve outside the strips is, of course, under the full steam pressure in the steam-chest. It is necessary to have a certain amount of pressure on the back of the valve to keep it on its seat on the port facing, and this pressure should be somewhat greater than the cylinder pressure underneath, which tends to lift it. On the other hand, should water accumulate in the cylinders, resulting in excessive pressure, the valve should be able to lift slightly to allow this to escape.

The area enclosed within the frame, or the balanced area, is usually made equal to the area of one steam-port plus the area of the exhaust

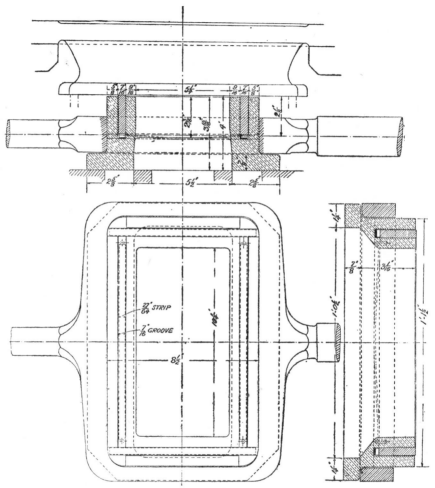

FIG. 7.—BALANCED SLIDE-VALVE.

port, and the two bridges between the ports. The area should be measured from the outside of the strips. To obtain a free, direct exhaust to the blast-pipe, many engines have been built provided with balanced slide-valves having an exhaust passage through the back. A valve of this type is shown in Fig. 7.

The balanced area is contained within a frame, as already described. Rectangular grooves, 2¼ in. deep by 7/16 in. wide, are cut in the back of the gun-metal valve. Into this fit four cast-iron strips, each $2\frac{3}{16}$ in.

deep by 27/64 in. wide, which form the frame.   The strips are pressed against a pressure plate fixed to the steam-chest cover by means of bent steel springs placed in the bottoms of the grooves.   The exhaust passage is made through the pressure plate and steam-chest cover, and it is by this that the exhaust steam passes straight to the blast-pipe.

Piston Valves.

As already mentioned, in recent years slide-valves of locomotives have undergone much modification, and piston valves have almost entirely superseded the flat D-valves.   The advent of superheated steam,

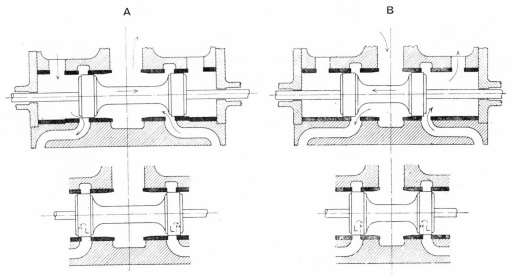

FIG. 8.—PISTON VALVES.

with development of higher pressures, has made this change a necessity. A piston valve consists of two pistons attached to a spindle, as shown in Fig. 8, moving to and fro inside a cylindrical steam-chest.   In (A) the boiler steam pressure acts on both outside faces of the pistons, and in (B) on the inside faces.   The pressure acting upon one face balances that of the other, hence the force required to move the valve has to overcome frictional resistance only—which is estimated at from one-fifth to one-sixth of that for an ordinary D slide-valve of equivalent size.

The principal advantage of piston valves is that they can be perfectly balanced, since pressure does not act, as in the D-valve, on the surface of the back, pressing it against the valve face of the cylinders.   Disadvantages are that piston valves are more complicated, more expensive, as well as having to incorporate special construction for allowing condensed steam in the form of water to escape from the cylinder. In the case of the ordinary slide-valve, the excessive pressure produced by any trapped water inside the clearance space of the cylinder lifts the valve and allows itself to escape. Piston valves being held rigidly within the cylindrical chambers, they move in, cannot lift, and therefore some special means must be devised, either in the construction of the valves themselves or by the addition of relief valves in the clearance spaces, otherwise serious danger may be incurred with the cylinders or covers; the latter may be knocked out. In early examples, no provision was made for this possibility, and much damage was done to cylinders and valve-gear, resulting in piston valves falling into disfavour for a time. Development in size of cylinders and valves, and perfecting of means for meeting the condition above referred to have had their results, and piston valves are now generally employed.

The conditions essential to satisfactory working of piston valves are that they must be steam-tight, and not allow any " live " steam to leak past the pistons into the exhaust. The other need has been referred to above, namely, the release of trapped water. The condition of "tightness" is met by a careful design of the piston rings, and the means by which they are kept in close contact with the liners they move in. For the release of water, the piston rings may be made so that under excessive pressure the segments which compose them will contract and allow imprisoned water to escape to the exhaust. Various forms of release valve have also been introduced for this purpose, and those designed to open automatically when the pressure inside the clearances exceed a predetermined figure are favoured.

When steam is shut off and the engine is " coasting," as in running down a steep grade, the cylinder pistons act as pumps and create vacuum in the steam-chest. To destroy this, " snifting " valves are provided in the latter, which admit air from the outside. Some arrangements admit steam as well as air, which has the advantage of providing lubrication for the cylinder, pistons, and valves; it is also claimed to act as a cushion for the piston before this reaches the end of its stroke. In superheated engines, where the cushioning may become excessive, the cylinders are often supplied with by-pass connections; these may be combined with the water release valves.

With ordinary D slide valves, steam is admitted to the two steam-ports of the cylinder at the outside edges, therefore these can be said to have " outside admission." The piston valve shown in Fig. A also has outside admission, as the steam from the boiler enters the ports by the outside edges of the pistons in turn, and exhaust takes place in the space between the two pistons forming the valve; the action is accordingly precisely as that of the D-valves.

Outside admission, however, has certain disadvantages which become more serious with superheating and increased steam pressure; the latter necessarily exerting its full effect on the valve spindle stuffing-box. For these reasons practically all modern engines are arranged so that the steam from the boiler enters the space *between* the two pistons forming the valve, and is from there admitted to the cylinder. Fig. B shows this, wherein the valves are known as " inside admission " valves, exhaust taking place at the ends. The stuffing-box, in this case, is exposed only to low-pressure exhaust steam.

With outside admission valves, the steam lap is outside and known as " outside lap," in contra-distinction, for that of inside admission valves, wherein the steam lap would be on the inside, the lap is shown by L on the respective Fig. 8 A and B. Similarly, the exhaust lap—or exhaust clearance—if any, is on the outside of the valve. The lead of the valve is necessarily on the same side as the steam lap. It must be noted that the direction of movement of the valve is reversed in the case of inside admission. In Fig. 8 A with outside admission, the valve is moved to the right to admit steam to the left-hand port; but in B the movement is to the left. Needless to say, this reversal of movement requires important modifications in the arrangement of the valve-gear.

It will be noticed in the diagrams, Fig. 8, that the piston valves work inside bushes, or liners, which are fitted into the cylinder casting. When wear takes place, these bushes can be replaced and the cylinder casting remain unaffected. Holes are made in the liners opposite the valve chamber, and these are bridged over at intervals with straight, or diagonal, bars.

The piston valve rings and ports in the liners should be carefully designed, so that there is no possibility of the rings catching in them, and so breaking. Narrow rings wear the surfaces and bridges of the ports more quickly than those areas over which the rings do not move. The result is that ridges are formed whereon the rings are liable to catch and break. The best form for the steam-passages through the liner is a series of triangular openings separated by right and left bars, alternately.

A successful form of piston valve largely adopted on locomotives is given in the dimensioned drawing, Fig. 9, where provision for the escape of water will be observed. The valve spindle is fitted with a facing and nut, between which a steel cap is secured, as shown. This cap has three double horns, the spaces between which form radial grooves. It is maintained in position by a key let into the spindle. Next to the cap is the piston ring itself, which is given in detail in the lower illustration.

Trofimoff Piston Valves.

In the ingenious arrangement, Fig. 10, provision is made for the piston heads to move longitudinally along the spindle between the two end-plates; the drawing shows the arrangement of one head. When the regulator is open the pressure of the steam between the piston heads holds them firmly against the ends, as if mechanically secured to the

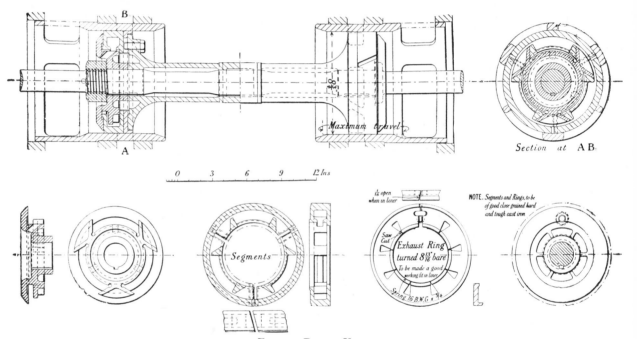

Fig. 9.—Piston Valve.

valve spindle, but when steam is shut off the piston heads remain stationary at the end of their travel about the centre of the steam-chest, uncovering the steam-ports and providing free communication from one end of the cylinder to the other. Considerable economies are claimed for this device.

Stuffing-boxes.

Another important detail of locomotive cylinders is the stuffing-box, through which the piston-rod, or valve-spindle, passes. With super-heaters, the high temperature of the steam necessitates using metallic packing, as also special means of lubrication. Fig. 11 gives one of the most approved designs. In this the packing rings are of white metal

retained in the stuffing-box by a cap in which a strong spiral spring is
housed.   The object of this spring is to keep the white metal rings

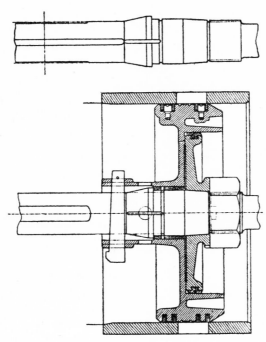

FIG. 10.—THE TROFIMOFF PISTON VALVE.

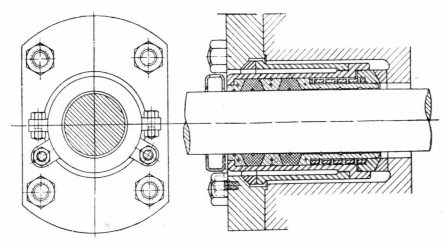

FIG. 11.—STUFFING-BOX WITH METALLIC PACKING.

forced up against the casing so that they tend to close in on the
piston-rod, so ensuring a steam-tight working surface between the rod
and the rings.

Stephenson Gear.

Valve-gears vary considerably in their details; the Stephenson, or shifting-link motion, is, perhaps, the most popular for locomotives of any link gear. There are two eccentrics for each cylinder, fixed side by side upon the driving axle, one for moving the valves for running forward, the other for backward. The ends of the eccentric rods are connected to a quadrant link, the fore-gear at the bottom. A quadrant block carried by the intermediate valve spindle slides in the slot of the link, so that if this latter is lowered the block is nearer the top of the link, and the eccentric will operate the valve, to enable the engine to move in the forward direction; then, if the link is lifted, the bottom, or back-gear, eccentric and rod will be brought into co-operation for the engine to move backward.

The link in mid-position causes the eccentrics to neutralize each other, and there is practically no movement imparted to the valve. In Fig. 12, A shows the link connected up at the centre, with the reversing shaft above; the swing links hang down to connect with the saddle-pins. A modification of this device allows for the reversing shaft to be below; the swing links then have to be extended up to the saddle-pins, In B, the reversing shaft is above, and the swing links reach down to the bottom of the link and are connected through the same pins as the back-gear eccentric rods. In C, the arrangement is reversed, the swing links being coupled to the fore-gear eccentric rod-pin at the top of the link.

A condition which affects steam distribution is the differences in the position of the piston caused by the " angularity " of the connecting rod when the events of cut-off, release, etc., take place; that is to say, in the out-stroke towards the crank, the effect will be later than on the opposite, or in-stroke. The shorter the connecting rod the greater will be these inequalities. Fig. 13 illustrates this: AB is the stroke of the piston, and aC_1b the circular path of the crankpin. If the crank be at OC_1 when steam is cut off on the out-stroke, the position of the piston will be at P_1, and AP_1 represents the distance through which the piston has travelled. On the return, or in-stroke, the crank is at OC_2 when cut-off takes place, and the piston has travelled through a distance of BP_2, which is less than AP_1. The difference can be shown in another way. Supposing the crank OC_3 be vertical, the piston will be at Q, and has travelled a distance of AQ on the out-stroke; on the in-stroke, the crank is in the corresponding position, OC_1, with the piston also at Q; but the distance BQ is less than AQ. For if, with the centre Q and radius QC_3, equal to the length of connecting rod, the arc C_3qC_4 be drawn, cutting ab in q, aq will be equal to AQ, and bq equal to BQ. The point q lies on that side of the centre O away from the piston. Angularity of the eccentric rods produce a similar effect on the position of the

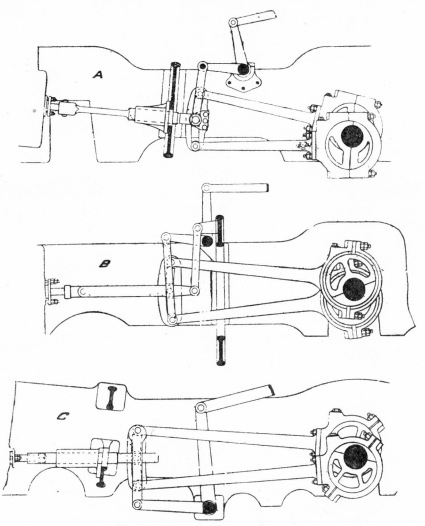

FIG. 12.—STEPHENSON GEAR.

valves, but to a much smaller extent, as the ratio of length of the rods to the radius of the eccentric is usually very large, except in the case of very short rods.

Other link motions associated with the names of Allan and Gooch are well known, and have been dealt with in so many text-books that description here is unnecessary. The Stephenson (shifting-link) we have described, as this was, and still is, much used for locomotives. The

Gooch (stationary link) was favoured on the continent of Europe, and had a number of installations in this country; whilst the Allen (straight link) never attained very great adoption here, beyond the locomotives of the railway on which it originated.

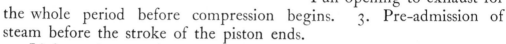

FIG. 13.

An ideal valve-gear should give: 1. Full steam admission, with quick opening and closing of the ports for all degrees of cut-off. 2. Full opening to exhaust for the whole period before compression begins. 3. Pre-admission of steam before the stroke of the piston ends.

Link motions, and even radial gears, have not as yet been built to completely fulfil these ideal functions. They give high mechanical efficiency, are simple in action, and also easy to maintain. Gears operated by " cams " give results more closely approximating the ideal, but, although many are in service, it is yet early to say that in practical working they meet every condition.

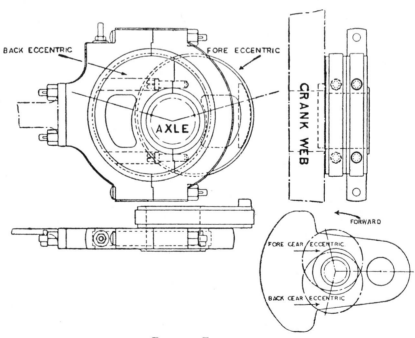

FIG. 14.—ECCENTRICS.

Eccentrics.

Eccentric sheaves, with their straps and connections, form most important details of the locomotive's motion. In Fig. 14 a pair—that is, the fore and back—are shown as they would appear attached to the crank-axle; these, of course, communicate their motion to the expansion links, as shown in the diagram of the Stephenson motion. The sheaves are in two portions, held together by bolts passing through which are secured by cotters, driven through holes, as shown. They are usually cast in pairs. The straps have liners inside the bearing on the sheaves; these liners are often of brass.

Walschaerts Gear.

The radial valve-gear which probably has most general adoption at the time of writing is the Walschaert, which, although invented as long

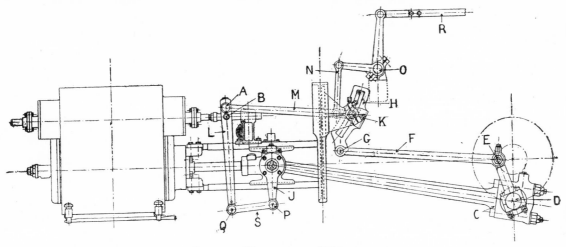

FIG. 15.—WALSCHAERTS GEAR.

ago as 1844, has only during the last thirty-five years received the attention it deserved. Its accessibility, light weight, and general mechanical efficiency have done much towards its general adoption.

Various modifications of the Walschaerts gear have been proposed and several are in use; as it has become such an important detail in our modern locomotives, it will now be fully described. Fig. 15 shows it as used on a British locomotive, the motion of the valve being obtained from two independent movements.

Movement A, taken through links from the crosshead of the engine, provides a travel equal to twice the steam lap plus twice the lead, which is equal to the steam lap plus the lead on either side of the central position; the remaining portion of the valve travel, which gives a port opening on each side greater than the lead, is derived from a return crank upon the crankpin.

The crosshead has a bottom tailpiece J, which is connected with the union link S to the combination lever L. The upper end of this lever L is attached at B to the valve spindle, and at A to the end of the radius rod M. In mid-gear, rod M (as will be explained later) has no movement, and therefore A is then a fixed fulcrum. Point Q has a total movement equal to that of P, or the stroke of the piston, and the lengths of the lever arms QB and QA are such that the point B of the valve spindle moves a total distance equal to the lap plus the lead on each side of its central position. With the portion of the mechanism just described, the valve is opened at each end by an amount equal to the lead, which is constant for all positions of the gear.

The second movement is derived from the return crank E attached to the crankpin D, which rotates with the crank axle, and through the rod F actuates the slotted expansion link H to which it is attached at the tailpiece G. The link oscillates about the fixed trunnion K. Inside the slot a die, or block, works, attached to the back end of the radius rod M, the front end of the latter being pinned at the point A to the combination lever L. The illustration gives the gear in mid-position, the centre of the die block coinciding with the centre of the trunnion K. As link H simply oscillates about K, it is obvious that in this mid-gear position no movement is imparted by the link to the radius rod M. By moving the reversing rod R forward to the left, the lever arms rotate through an angle about the reversing shaft O, and the lifting link N, which is attached to M, is lowered, and with it the die block, which drops into the lower portion of the slot. This is the fore-gear position in which the movement of the link imparts a reciprocating movement to M, and a travel of the valve additional to that already produced by the combination lever. If the die block be raised by N into the upper portion of the slot, the movement of M is reversed, since the link which actuates the block is pivoted about its centre K. The amount of additional travel imparted to the valve will depend upon the position of the die in the slot; the further the die is from K the greater will be the travel.

The gear is usually so arranged that the die is in the bottom half of the link for "forward" gear, as the line of action between the connecting rod F and valve rod N is then more direct, and extra strains due to the angular positions of the rods are avoided. In a tank engine, which runs equally in both directions, the position of the block in the upper portion of the slot for "fore-gear" can be arranged, if desired, and many such engines are found with this modification.

With single eccentric gear of the Walschaerts type, the return crank must be at right angles to the crankpin, in order to enable the engine to run either forward or backward. A slight deviation from the angle of 90° is sometimes given, for reasons which will be mentioned.

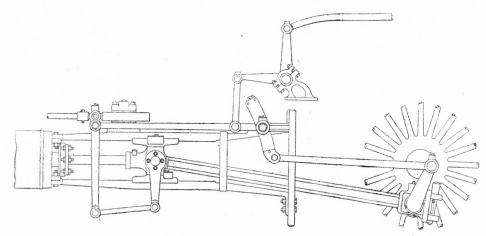

FIG. 16.—WALSCHAERTS GEAR.

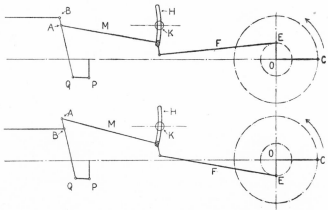

FIG. 17.—DIAGRAM OF WALSCHAERTS GEAR.

In Fig. 16 an arrangement of gear for a French compound locomotive is shown, fitted for slide-valves with outside admission.

In the next figure, Fig. 17, it will be seen that for forward running the eccentric OE leads the crank OC by an angle of 90° with the usual arrangement and the block at the bottom of the link. No angle of advance above 90° is necessary, as in the case of the Stephenson link motion, since the lap and lead in Walschaerts gear are controlled by the combination lever and crosshead connection. Further, for outside admission, the valve rod M is connected to the combination lever at a point A, below B, where the valve spindle is connected to the same lever. Similar conditions are found with outside admission piston valves.

For piston valves with inside admission, two modifications are needed, as shown in the lower diagram, so as to open the port to steam, the valve must move in the opposite direction. First, the eccentric OE, in this case, must follow the crank OC by 90° instead of leading it in forward gear; and second, the connections with combination lever must be reversed. The radius rod M is now connected at A above the point B, where the valve spindle is connected. These two figures have letters corresponding with those in the original drawing, Fig. 15.

It was stated in the preceding paragraphs that the eccentric was placed 90° from the crank; theoretically, this is the correct position if the connection of the eccentric rod F with the projection G of the link, Fig. 15 is on the centre line of the cylinders and crank-axle. This position, however, is not always possible, and it will be noticed that joint G is shown above the centre line. The connecting rod F should be as nearly coincident with the centre line of the engine as possible when the crank C is at its lowest point, as shown; this, probably, would make the projection G of the link too long, and shorten the throw of the link, unless the radius of the path of E is increased. To modify the error introduced by the angular position of the eccentric rod, the centre of the eccentric is moved round slightly for fore-gear from the 90° position through a small angle of 3° or 4°. In the case of an engine with outside admission, the eccentric would then be placed to lead the crank by an angle of 90° minus this amount; whilst with inside admission, the eccentric follows the crank by an angle of 90° plus this amount.

The condition is not an " angle of advance " in the sense in which it is used for the Stephenson and other link motions; in other words, it is not for the purpose of producing lap and lead. The above modification of the angular position of the return crank applies to fore-gear, and is applicable to tender engines which run chiefly with the chimney in the forward direction. Any such alteration will alter the distribution in back-gear for the worse, and, therefore, for tank engines running equally in both directions, it is better to retain the original position of 90° from the crank.

Fig. 18 gives in full, details of an arrangement in which the radius rod is shifted, and the slotted portion of the rod placed ahead of the crank, thus eliminating the back extension of the radius rod. This example indicates a way of fitting the supports of the reversing arm-shaft, so that these

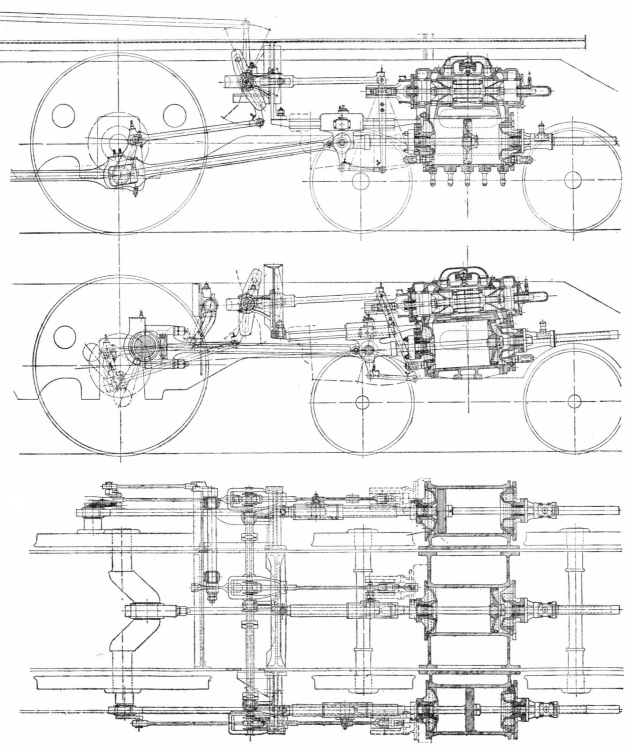

FIG. 18.—MODIFIED WALSCHAERTS VALVE GEAR, L.N.E.R.

also serve indirectly to carry the link trunnions which work in bearings located in the sides of a stirrup formed upon the extremity of the reversing arm-shaft. Forward extensions of this stirrup take hold of a die block, sliding in a slot in the radius rod, by which the latter is moved up or down in the link. The centres of oscillation of the links and of the reversing arm-shaft are coincident, and the latter being made sufficiently rigid to sustain the links, the only supports required are the brackets for the reversing arm-shaft. This arrangement has been applied to a great number of locomotives both at home and abroad.

In modern British locomotives with four cylinders, and simple expansion, each cylinder has its own valve, the connections between the valve spindles being made by means of a horizontal rocking lever, the ends of which are attached to the respective valve spindles, so that

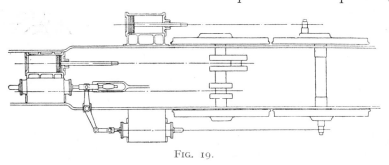

Fig. 19.

the interconnected valves reciprocate in opposite directions, in harmony with the pistons, the latter, of course, driving cranks having a relative angularity of 180°.

In four-cylinder 4-6-0 type locomotives, as many on the G.W. Railway, the Walschaert gear is arranged inside the frames, as shown in diagram, Fig. 19. The rocking lever is placed behind the inside cylinder and in front of the outside cylinder.

The next figure, No. 19 A, illustrates the arrangement as adopted on certain four-cylinder 4-6-0 express engines of the L.M. & S. Railway. In this the Walschaert gear is exterior, with the rocking lever in front of both cylinders.

Another modification, as Fig. 19 B, is adopted on other engines of the L.M. & S. Railway. In this the rocking lever is arranged on the crank-axle side of the cylinders.

In comparing the foregoing it may be noted that in Fig. 19 A the inside cylinder valve is subject to displacement, due to the cumulative effect of the expansion of the valve spindles by the heat of the steam, since an outside spindle in expanding pushes the end of the lever connected to its tail spindle, movement is transferred to the spindle of the inside valve, which also expands to some extent in the presence of steam. In setting the valve of this cylinder, therefore, allowance must be made for expansion.

On some of the four-cylinder engines of the L. & N.E. Railway a somewhat different arrangement is in use. Here a horizontal shaft unites the valves of the adjacent cylinders, on each side by means of

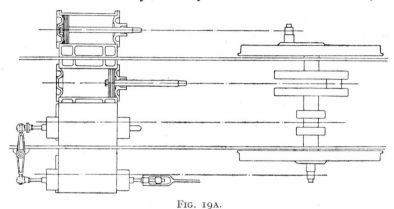

FIG. 19A.

vertical arms, the ends of which consequently move simultaneously in the same direction, and as one valve is meant for inside admission and the other for outside, and the cranks are set at 180° with reference to each other, the same effect is secured as with rocking levers working two identical valves travelling in opposition. This design, like that in

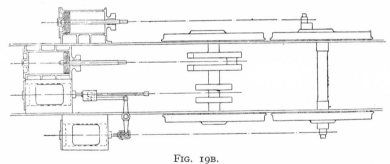

FIG. 19B.

Fig. 19 b, has the merit of affording easy access to the valves of all four cylinders without unnecessarily dismounting the rocking gear.

In arrangements where there are two sets of valve-gear driving two valves only, each valve serving to distribute the steam to the two cylinders, there are numerous examples in foreign practice, but in this country there appears to be but one example and that is a four-cylinder simple expansion 0-10-0 tank engine on the L.M. & S. Railway, in which the steam ports of the outside cylinders are direct, and those to the inside cylinders are crossed. Generally, any system of cross-porting is not to be favoured, although it probably offers no practical disadvantage in the case of a locomotive assigned to such exceptional duties as are allocated to the engine mentioned above.

The advantages of the Walschaerts gear are many, and there is no doubt in its present form it represents a valve-gear well adapted to the requirements of steam locomotives. Theoretically, it may be inferior to some gears which have been devised, but its good steam distribution, its simplicity, lightness and suitability for plain D or piston valves, with either " inside " or " outside " admission, its easy operation (the reversing gear having only to move a comparatively light radius rod instead of the whole mass of a link and two eccentric rods) and applicability in the best position for the valves, *i.e.* outside and above the cylinders, with the centre line of the valve spindle and piston-rod parallel, all combine to make it a most satisfactory gear.

Before leaving the subject of valves and valve-gears, it may be stated that the number of arrangements which have been invented for the purpose of improving the distribution of steam in the cylinders of locomotives is legion. Many have been tried, but few adopted to any extent. One of the shortcomings of the ordinary slide-valve is the slow opening and closing of the steam-ports, especially at early cut-off, since the linear speed of the valve is greatly reduced when the gear is " notched up," thus causing " wire-drawing," or a fall of pressure during admission, owing to the reduction in the volume of steam in its passage through the restricted areas provided. Piston valves are an improvement on this, for the reason that the circular port area can be made much larger than the rectangular ports of slide-valves. The speed, however, with which the valves are moved into their correct positions for cutting-off, etc., can only be influenced by the operating gear.

In the case of large stationary and marine engines, the disadvantages of the slide-valve have long since caused its replacement with other forms, but the restricted space available on locomotives have somewhat handicapped advancement in this respect.

Corliss Valves.

The Corliss gear, in which slide-valves are replaced by oscillating valves operated by a gear which gives quick and sudden movements, has been used in different designs for forty odd years past, and in Fig. 20 an arrangement is illustrated which has been adopted on a number of outside cylinder express engines on French railways; this will serve to show how such devices can be utilized. In this case the gear was of the Gooch, or stationary link type, and, referring to the letters, the link C is extended at its upper end to accommodate a large double link block to which the admission and exhaust valve rods are jointed. The rod A is the admission valve rod, and is connected to the rod G, operating the oscillating Corliss valves H through the lever arms FF. The rod B works the exhaust valves through the rocking shaft J and rods K and L. As in stationary engine practice, exhaust valves are placed at the bottom of the cylinder, so that any condensed water can drain away. The cut-off is varied by shifting the block in the link C. As the exhaust rod B is arranged above the admission rod A, and therefore farther away from the centre of the link C, the amplitude of the movement of B will be greater than that of rod A for any given position of the link block in fore-gear when it is above the centre of the link. Rod B will, therefore, impart a greater

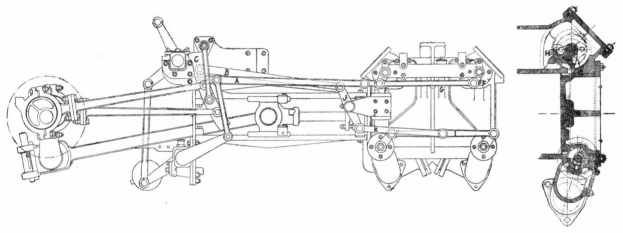

FIG. 20.—CORLISS TYPE VALVE-GEAR.

movement with more prolonged opening to the exhaust than to the admission valves. On the other hand, the distribution in back-gear has to be sacrificed, as when the engine is reversed the block will be below the centre of the link and the greater movement given to A.

For an admission up to 20 per cent. cut-off, the compression with this gear takes place through only 18 per cent. of the stroke, as compared with 36 per cent. on similar engines with the ordinary link motion. The gear, in spite of its complications, appears to have been very successful in steam economy, and probably would have been more largely used had not compounding become so popular on French railways.

Poppet Valves.

Following the principle of oscillating valves, the next development must be considered, namely, the introduction of " cam " operated

" poppet " valves. Fig. 21 shows an arrangement of rotary cam poppet valve-gear applied to a 2-6-0 mixed traffic locomotive. It has an outside main drive operating the cams inside the steam-chest, or cam-box, on the cylinder; the drive and the reversing gear connections are given. Each cylinder is fitted with a cam-box, complete with reversing section, and with a revolving cam-shaft carrying " fore-" and " back-" gear cams for the steam and exhaust valves. The valves are actuated by the cams through intermediate levers fitted in the cam-box and

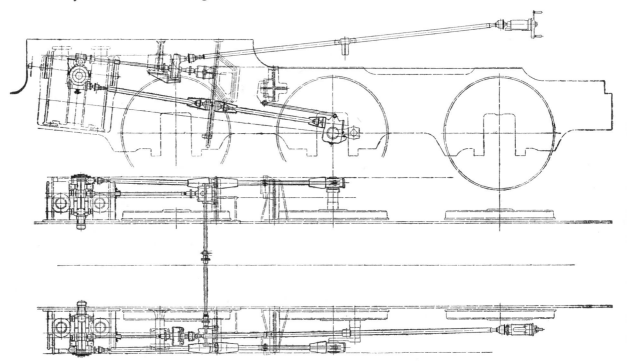

FIG. 21.—GENERAL ARRANGEMENT OF R.C. POPPET VALVE-GEAR ON L.M. & S. RAILWAY 2-6-0 MIXED TRAFFIC LOCOMOTIVE.

fulcrumed at their lower ends, whilst their upper ends abut on tappets, which, in turn, bear on the valve spindles. These levers are fitted with rollers which run on the profiles of the cams. The reversing and alterations in cut-off are obtained by moving the cam-shafts transversely, so that the desired cam profile will make contact with the rollers and through them operate the valves. The reversing gear consists of a rack gear with a pinion contained in the upper part of the cam-box. A stirrup is fitted to the rack, and at its lower extremity it spans the cam-shaft between the ball thrust washers. Rotation of the pinion moves the rack, and therefore the cam-shafts. The reversing gear for each cam-box is coupled together by means of a cross-shaft and enclosed bevel gear; connection to the driver's control in the cab of the engine is through a reduction gear and universal shaft. The main drive is in duplicate, and each is made up of the RC return crank gear-box, with anchor link, and the necessary universal driving shafts. Worm and wheel gears are used both in the return crank gear-boxes and in the cam-boxes, and anti-friction bearings are applied to the worm shaft in the upper part of the return crank gear-boxes, at the intermediate bearings at the motion-plate, and also in the cam-boxes.

The cylinders of the engine fitted are of standard pattern used with the RC poppet valve-gear for two-cylinder engines, having outside cylinders. They have main steam and exhaust connections of ample section and straight, short ports between the valves and the cylinders. The engine under notice has two cylinders 21 in. diameter, with a stroke of 26 in.; the coupled drivers are 5 ft. 6 in. diameter, and the radial truck wheels 3 ft. 6½ in.

Fig. 22 gives details of the oscillating cam poppet valve-gear. From this diagram it will be seen that the axes of the valves at either end of the cylinder are concentric, inasmuch as the spindle of the exhaust valve is a hollow tube through which passes the admission valve spindle. The hollow exhaust valve spindle is guided and supported by a long cylindrical passage in the member forming the inner seat of the exhaust valve, and also has its extended outer extremity guided by a suitable cavity in the inlet valve seat. The inlet valve spindle, in return, is guided and supported by the exhaust valve spindle, and additionally by an extension working in a passage formed within the cover; this gives access to the valve cages, etc.

All double-beat poppet valves are so fashioned that the diameter of one face slightly exceeds that of the other, thus ensuring a differential pressure from the steam, which, while insufficient to impose any great resistance to the opening of the valve, secures a steam-tight seating. Further, to compensate for the minute variations inevitable between the relative locations of the valve seats, despite every precaution in manufacture and fitting, the body of the valve is so made that its walls are sufficiently flexible to allow both faces to seat truly within the limits of distortion possible in the valve seatings.

In most poppet valve systems—including the Lentz arrangement—the valves are returned to their seats partly by the differential pressure, due to the unequal diameters of the seats, and partly by the action of coil springs. These springs have been eliminated in the new design, and, although little trouble was experienced in practice from this source, the simplification due to their abandonment is considered an advantage.

Their place is taken by steam pressure acting upon the small area of the spindle rod extremities. Steam, which also conveys lubricant, is introduced through a pipe to the admission spindle guide in the chamber cover, and, finally, passes through a passage bored in the spindle to the guiding space in the admission valve seat. Thus the steam acts upon the effective areas of the inlet and exhaust valve spindles, constantly

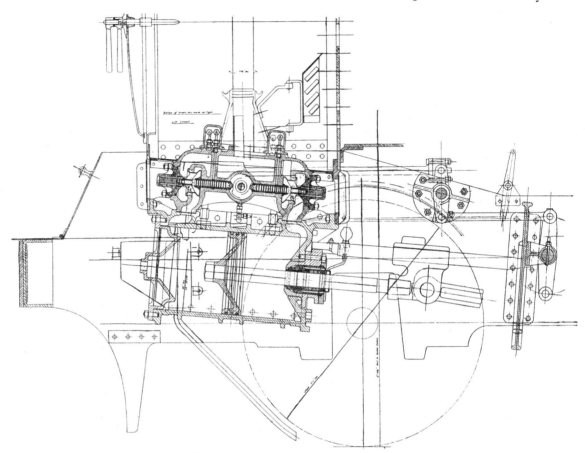

FIG. 22.—LENTZ POPPET VALVE-GEAR.

tending to return the valves to their respective seats, and, as the steam is taken directly from the boiler, the pressure is available at all times, no matter whether the engine be running light or under steam. Steam tightness is secured by the provision of grooves in the circumference of the spindles, so forming a labyrinth—a method which has long been in successful use for this purpose, with good lubrication.

The cam-gear for operating the valves is of great interest. A cam-shaft, supported by a single and very long bearing, lies midway across the cylinder. The face of the cam is of simple contour, and is symmetrical save for two clearance spaces in its upper portion. The faces of the cams make rolling contact with levers, of which the fulcra are fixed to the body of the cam-box. These levers press against the valve spindles, the effect of the levers being to amplify the movement of the spindles derived from the cam, and also to relieve the spindle faces from the angular thrust that would be set up if the radius of oscillation were excessively restricted.

In order to allow the levers to make proper contact, the outer, or exhaust, valve spindle is slotted for a part of its length, and the lever which acts upon it has a forked extremity. The lever for the inner inlet valve spindle, on the contrary, is single, and can therefore oscillate between the exhaust valve and within the spindle slot, when the relative positions of the two spindles cause the outer one to protrude over the end of the inner spindle. A device is incorporated whereby the valves may be held open, if required, so that a free passage is provided when drifting. As the cam is of the oscillating type, it is obvious that this valve arrangement can be actuated by any form of reciprocating gear, as is the case with other oscillating cam systems.

Reversing Gear.

The various valve motions described all require means for operation from the footplate so that the driver can, at will, not only reverse the engine, but regulate expansion of the steam in the cylinders by adjusting the cut-off to any point of the stroke he may require. The details of the appliances used for this purpose vary greatly; they are uniformly placed in the cab on what is termed the " driver's side," and arranged for convenient manipulation by him. Fig. 23 gives a few of the more common arrangements.

At A is shown a reversing lever, having a handle and trigger at one end and working on a pin passing through a plate and bracket at the other, the trigger is coupled to a rod passing down the lever to a catch sliding in a guide; when down this engages in slots or notches at the top of the plate, which is cut to a radius equal to the distance from the pivot of the lever; the notches are cut in separate sector plates set on each side of the lever, the catch being broad enough to engage both sectors, thus holding the lever firmly. When the catch is in the central notch the engine is out of gear, raising the catch by the trigger and pushing the lever over towards the front puts the motion into fore-gear and pulling it back the reverse, the intermediate notches giving different grades of expansion. The trigger may be as shown, on the back of the lever, or it may be placed upon the front, a spring being provided to keep the catch down in its notch, as otherwise it would be liable to work

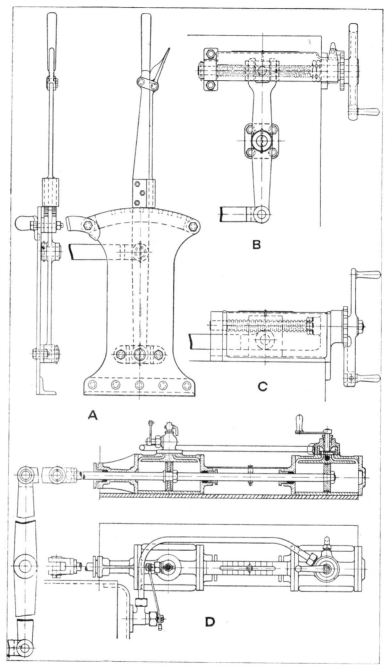

FIG. 23.—REVERSING ARRANGEMENTS.

up when the engine is running and allow the lever to be thrown violently
to the front or back of its travel, according to the position of the valve-

gear, which might have unpleasant results. The spring may be flat, situated between the trigger and handle as shown, or it may be coiled and attached to the bottom of the catch-rod, with one end secured to a hook in the lever; another mode of attachment is by a bracket fitted above the catch, the catch-rod passing through it, and the coiled spring being on the rod between the catch and bracket. A boss is provided at a point in the length of the lever and having a pinhole for the attachment of the forked end of the reversing rod, which at its other end is coupled to the arm of the reversing shaft. A bracket is fixed to the side of the plate for the driver to place his foot upon and so increase his power to pull the lever over.

In the above lever the reversing rod is coupled to an arm projecting up from the reversing shaft, but cases where these arms are carried downwards, the lever is then made much longer and pivoted at or near its centre, the lower half being carried down below the footplate and the rod coupled to it there.

A modification of this lever, fitted with a screw at the top instead of the handle, is shown at B. The lever has a forked end at the top and is fitted with a pair of sliding blocks, which work upon projecting pins upon the nut through which the screw revolves; it is pivoted at its centre, and being usually coupled to an arm projecting up from the reversing shaft, the top of the lever stands over to the back when the engine is in forward, and to the front in backward gear. The pivot may be, as shown, fixed to the side of the tank, or in the case of tender engines, which have no tanks, it is fixed to a separate plate attached to the frame beneath it. The screw is cut with a multiple thread so that the movement of the nut, and with it the lever, may be as quick as possible; it is carried in brackets at each end, and fitted with a wheel by which the driver may operate it. The wheel has attached to it a circular notched plate and, upon the bracket carrying the bearing for the screw, a catch is provided which can be dropped into the corresponding notch of the plate, thus securing the screw in any required position, as the thrust upon the nut when the engine is running is liable to cause the screw to revolve and put the motion into full gear. Above the screw and nut a guard or cover is fixed, having at its top a slot of a length equal to the travel of the nut, from which a pointer projects up and indicates upon a scale marked upon the face of the guard the point of cut-off the gear is in.

Another method of applying the screw is represented at C, in which the lever is dispensed with altogether, and the reversing rod coupled directly to the nut upon the screw. The screw is cut with a coarse thread as before, and carried in a pair of brackets, but instead of a wheel a pair of arms with handles set opposite to each other are employed. The handle at the top, in the illustration, is fixed to its arm and used to turn the screw, but that shown at the bottom is hinged and attached to a catch which it raises or lowers into notches in a ring fixed to the screw-bracket casting, to enable the gear to be secured in any position. A cover and index is fitted as in the last case.

Many engines have an arrangement exactly the reverse of the above, the screw being attached directly to the reversing rod, whilst the nut, forming one with the boss of the wheel and being revolved with it, pulls or pushes the screw and reverses the motion from one gear to another.

The lever has the advantage of being quickly moved from one full gear to the other, and therefore is especially suitable for shunting-engines; its disadvantage is that the notches, which have to be spaced widely for strength, frequently cause too great a difference in the rate of expansion when the catch is moved from one notch to the next, so that expedients are often resorted to by drivers to give a less difference, a common one being that of placing a piece of metal across the notches so that the catch will bear against it and hold the lever in a midway position. In the Norris lever, much used in the U.S.A., two catches are employed, one on either side of the lever, spaced to half a notch, and the catches being made with tapered ends, one or the other will always engage in the sector plate at half the travel of the plain lever. The advantages of the screw are the ease with which the engine can be reversed with steam on, and the great range of positions which it has.

In order to quickly and easily reverse the valve motion many arrangements of reversing gears, working by steam or compressed air, have been devised. One of these, operated by steam, is shown at D. Upon the top of the trailing splasher, inside the cab, two cylinders, each about 5 in. diameter by 9 in. stroke are fixed, with pistons both secured to the same rod, so that they move together. The cylinder shown on the right is for steam, and has the usual ports, one to each end of the cylinder, and one to exhaust between them. Upon the port face is a flat bottom disc valve, revolved by means of a handle above, which has a cavity below wide enough and sufficiently upon one side of the vertical centre to cover one steam- and the exhaust-port, putting them into free communication with each other; upon the side of the disc opposite to the cavity is a hole through the valve itself, through which steam is admitted from above to the port below the disc, so that when the disc is turned, as shown, steam is admitted to the left port and the right port is open to the exhaust. When turned through half a revolution steam is admitted at the other port, and when turned a quarter of a revolution both ports are closed.

The cylinder on the left is filled with oil or water, and instead of the disc valve has a by-pass cock, and no exhaust port; opening the by-pass, which is done by giving the handle a partial revolution, allows the liquid to flow from one end of the cylinder to the other, as the steam pressure in the other cylinder may force it. Closing the valve separates the liquid in each end and locks the piston in its position. The steam cock upon the cylinder is coupled to the by-pass cock and opens and closes with it. The piston in the steam cylinder is fitted with the ordinary spring ring, but that in the other cylinder is fitted with two cup leathers as shown; a cup is also provided upon the by-pass cock, so that any loss, due to leakage, etc., may be made up and all slack kept properly taken up.

The movement of the piston-rod is transmitted to the reversing shaft through a long lever, shown broken at the left of the sketch, and is coupled to a rod which connects it to the arm projecting down from the shaft. This gear is also fitted in other positions upon engines, often being arranged vertically as at the front end of the side tanks of tank engines.

The marks upon the scale indicating the gear and point of cut-off are found on the engine after it has been coupled up and had the valves set. Thus the cut-off points for the ports upon one side of the engine are determined as has been before described, and marks made upon the valve spindle, the crank is then set at the point in its stroke at which it is required to cut-off, this point being found on the slide bar, and the reversing gear moved until the valve exactly closes the front port, the point upon the scale that the pointer indicates is marked, and the wheels turned, with the reversing gear still in this position, until the back port closes and the position of the crosshead is noted. The crank is then set at the next position for which the cut-off is required, and the lever moved as before and the scale marked, and so on for all points in the forward gear, then the engine is reversed and similar points found for the backward gear. It is usual to mark the ends of the indicator with the words " fore " and " back," to show the gear the motion is in.

The tendency at the present time, with the common adoption of the Walschaerts gear, is to use the so-called " screw-reversing," as there is no longer the necessity to lift the heavy links of the ordinary link motion.

Crossheads.

The piston-rods of a locomotive are connected at the ends farthest from the cylinders to the crossheads, which may be of two or three forms: a block sliding between two bars, or four bars, or arranged to be guided by a single bar. In our typical example of a locomotive in the frontispiece the crosshead consists of a block sliding between four bars, and from it connection is taken for the Walschaert gear.

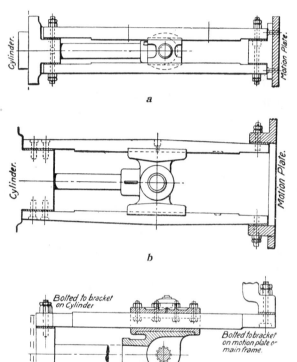

In Fig. 24 three (*a, b, c*) forms of crosshead are shown. The first (*a*) consists of four bars between which the block slides. The bars are carefully adjusted by packing-pieces placed under the ends, where they are secured to the cylinder and motion-plate respectively, as it is essential the bars should be parallel. The second (*b*) arrangement is composed of two bars only with the crosshead sliding in an upright position between them. A third (*c*) form is shown as a single bar which the crosshead encloses and slides on. The bar is supported at the cylinder end on a "lug" formed with the casting, and at the other is held to the motion-plate by a bolt with a head sunk into the bar.

FIG. 24.—CROSSHEADS.

The slides, or shoes, transmit to the bar, or bars, the pressure due to the angularity of the connecting rod and crank, as the former is being forced away from or drawn towards the cylinder. The greatest pressure is experienced on the top bar (or bars) when the engine is running forward, and on the bottom when running backward.

Connecting Rods.

The connecting rod couples up the crosshead with the crankpin and in the main connection for the transmission of power from the reciprocating motion of the piston-rod to the rotary motion of the crankpin.

There are many forms of connecting rod, and Fig. 25 shows those

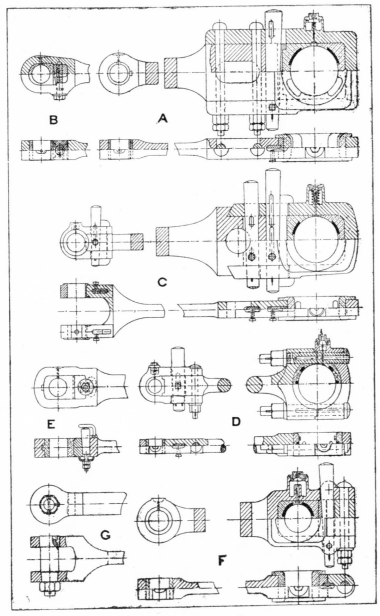

Fig. 25.—Connecting Rods.

more generally used. A is a strapped " big "-end with a solid eyed " small "-end. The jaws of the strap fit over two half-brasses, and on to the end of the rod, being held by two tapering bolts fitting very accurately and secured by lock nuts. The two brasses encircle the crankpin, and are held together with the necessary closeness to the journal by a long, flat, tapering cotter, a " push-plate " being inserted between the cotter and the front brass. The cotter is prevented from slackening by means of two set-screws in the strap above and below the rod end; it has a small cotter through its lower part. The cup for oil is forged solid with the strap, and machined to shape; each of the brasses has two hollows into which white metal is poured to form an antifriction bearing.

A large hole will be noticed cut through the " big "-end; this is to reduce weight. The " small "-end is bored out and fitted with a bush pressed in, and prevented from turning by a key. The rods, strap, and bolts are of steel machined all over.

B shows another " small "-end, also solid eyed, but provided with means for adjustment of the two brasses, so neutralizing wear. The wedge-shaped block can be raised or lowered by means of a screw-bolt, as shown, and is prevented from turning when set by a locking-plate placed over it, held by a split pin.

C gives another strapped " big "-end, with different means of securing strap and brasses. D illustrates the " marine " type " big "-end, which is used on some locomotives. The end of the rod is swelled out to take two long bolts—one above and the other below the crankpin; the brasses are held by the cap, and secured as shown. E, F and G illustrate other forms of the ends of connecting rods frequently met with in service.

Coupling Rods.

As previously mentioned, to secure necessary adhesion, locomotives have to have a number of their driving wheels coupled together. This entails the use of " coupling," or " side " rods, as they are termed, which, by means of the crankpins provided on the bosses of the driving wheels, enable these to be so connected together that all must revolve in unison, on power being applied to the main axle. These coupling rods are subjected to many stresses, so that manifestly if the weight of the rods can be kept down those stresses depending upon centrifugal force will be reduced. They are of steel of similar quality to that used for the connecting rods, and usually formed of one piece without weld; often special alloys are used to assist in securing lightness combined with strength. The cross-section may be of plain, rectangular shape, but more often is of " I " form; when very long the section is increased in depth, and sometimes in width, towards the centre where stresses are greatest. Fig. 26 gives details of several rods in general use, but the solid type shown at A is perhaps the most often met with; the bush

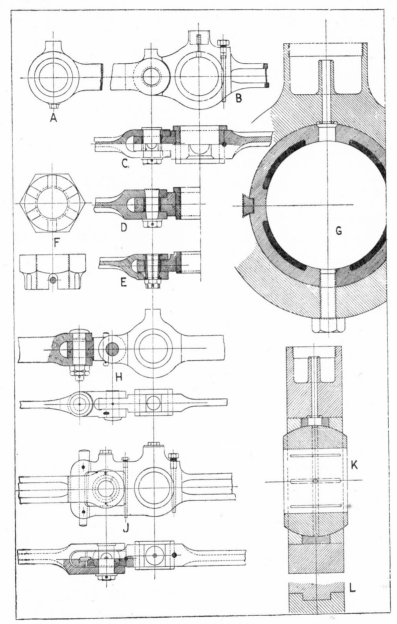

FIG. 26.—COUPLING ROD ENDS.

is usually of bronze, with a white metal lining, arranged as shown at G. The means taken to prevent it turning on the rod will be noticed, although it is becoming the practice to allow the bushes to turn in their own bearings. B is a tapered pin passing through a hole partly in the rod and partly in the bush.

Compared with others, the rods of four-coupled engines are comparatively simple, being a single piece with bushed ends as just described, or with "box" or strap ends, similar to those described under the heading of connecting rods. On engines having six or more pairs of coupled wheels, it is necessary that there should be freedom allowed for the rods to move vertically irrespective of each other, as the wheels to which they are attached assume varying levels when running. A joint to allow of this movement is shown at C, where the prolongation of one rod has an eye for the reception of a pin which also passes through a fork upon the other length. The hole in the first-mentioned rod is often bushed with a steel bush, and the pin made a tight fit and held in the fork by a feather, so that all the wear is taken up in the bush, which can be easily renewed.

A further development of the same joint is shown at D, where the pin is tapered and a better fit is thereby assured between it and the rod, thus reducing the tendency to knock. A more recent design still is that shown at E, where a joint pin of continuous taper fits into a steel bush split on one side. The taper pin is tightened or drawn up until the outside diameter of the bush entirely fills the hole in the rod, thereby securing a perfectly rigid fit. Fitted with a castellated nut, and screwed a fine thread, after the style at F, very fine adjustment may be made with this arrangement.

Another method is to fork one rod and form the other with a large eye to go between the jaws of the fork. These take a gun-metal bush large enough to form a seat for the crankpin. The fork is made a working fit upon the outside of the bush, and so the rods get the required hinge action. A longer crankpin is necessary in this case. Entirely separate rods are also to be seen, one of which will be close against the wheels and the other on journals provided upon the pins, which in this case will project out a much greater distance, as the rods work in quite different planes.

Engines having a long coupled wheel-base, such as those with 8, 10 or 12 wheels coupled and which have to negotiate curves of small radii, often have side play given to certain wheels. This means, therefore, that as well as allowing for vertical play, the coupling rods of such engines must be allowed lateral movement. Two ways of combining these movements are shown at H, J and K. In the type H, an intermediate piece is introduced, one end of which works on a horizontal pin, and the other on a vertical pin, thus allowing movement to take place only in the directly opposite direction respectively; a possible objection to this arrangement is the number of loose joints. A much more elaborate, but very successful arrangement is that shown at J. The attachment to the coupling rod is made by a pin which passes through a partly spherical solid bush shown to a larger scale at K. This bush is housed in a bearing, made in halves, and which is in turn held in the main rod by the taper cotter. To assemble these parts they must be together before being put into the rod, after which the taper pin locates one part of the bearing, while the cotter locates the other and tightens them both in place. The halves of the bearing are jointed at the centre line, as shown in plan L. One advantage that this form has over the type H is that it allows movement to take place in all directions. Considering the heavy wear and tear to which this joint is subjected, the bearings are made of mild steel, carbonized and hardened, and special attention is given to the method of lubrication.

The practice of forming solid oil-boxes, for the purpose of lubricating the knuckle-joint pin and faces (examples of which are shown at B and J), is widely adopted. British practice, with very few exceptions, is to form the oil-boxes solid with the rod. The stems are also often made solid, and the special recess at the bottom of the oil-hole is so made that the oil will form into globules, and afterwards drop on to the crankpin. Otherwise, the oil, on its way down the stem or pipe, might work its way between the rod and the bush with detrimental results.

In Fig. 27 an ingenious arrangement of connected drive is given, whereby the strains on the main crankpin of a coupled locomotive are distributed. The construction of the connecting rod and end of coupling rod is clearly shown, and the benefits claimed are also depicted in the diagram of a ten-coupled locomotive, showing plainly how the thrust from the main crankpin is distributed to the first and second pairs of coupled wheels. The big-end is slotted, and between the jaws the front end of the coupling rod. Both rods are fitted over a steel bush, which is held by a key in one of the big-end jaws. This in turn fits over a floating brass bush which can revolve inside the steel bush. The former revolves on the main crankpin, and the latter can, of course, turn inside it.

By this arrangement a larger bearing surface is obtained, and the centre lines of the coupling and connecting rods coincide, and in consequence relieve the crankpin of part of the load.

The small diagram, Fig. 28, clearly illustrates the distribution of the stresses in the case of a ten-coupled engine where the proportion of thrust delivered through the main crankpin and transmitted to the fourth and fifth pair of drivers is shown by a heavy solid line, while

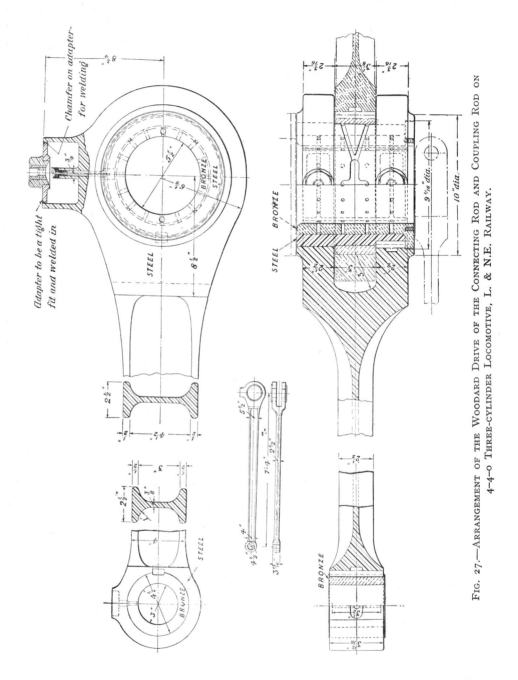

FIG. 27.—ARRANGEMENT OF THE WOODARD DRIVE OF THE CONNECTING ROD AND COUPLING ROD ON 4-4-0 THREE-CYLINDER LOCOMOTIVE, L. & N.E. RAILWAY.

that distributed through the bush to the first and second pairs of coupled wheels is represented by a cross-hatched line.

Roller Bearings.

Apart from effecting substantial reduction in friction, ball and roller bearings are characterized by the elimination of undue wear on rotating or oscillating parts.   The latter point is of particular importance where the bearings are exposed to the ingress of sand, grit and other abrasive matter.   Owing to the fact that ball and roller bearings can be lubricated with grease, instead of oil, the housing for the bearings can be readily

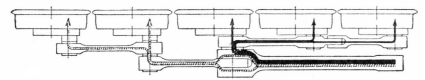

FIG. 28.—WOODARD DRIVE ON A TEN-COUPLED LOCOMOTIVE.

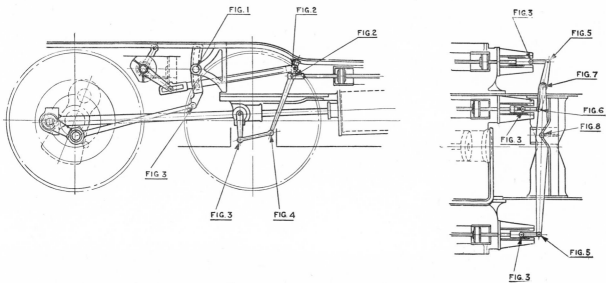

FIG. 29.—DIAGRAM OF THE WALSCHAERT-GRESLEY VALVE MOTION SHOWING POSITIONS OF
ROLLER BEARINGS.   THREE-CYLINDER L. & N.E. RAILWAY LOCOMOTIVES.

designed to retain the lubricant which effectively seals the open ends against the ingress of abrasive matter.

The accompanying drawing, Fig. 29, indicates the location of the various bearings in the valve-gear of a locomotive, in each case the journal load being taken on roller bearings. Fig. 30 (1 to 8) illustrates the various joints in detail numbered to correspond with the reference numbers on Fig. 29.   The rollers employed are cylindrical and the location of the link is effected by lips formed respectively on the outside of the outer race and the inside of the inner race. This arrangement has been found to give satisfactory location where the end thrust encountered is of a comparatively low order, as

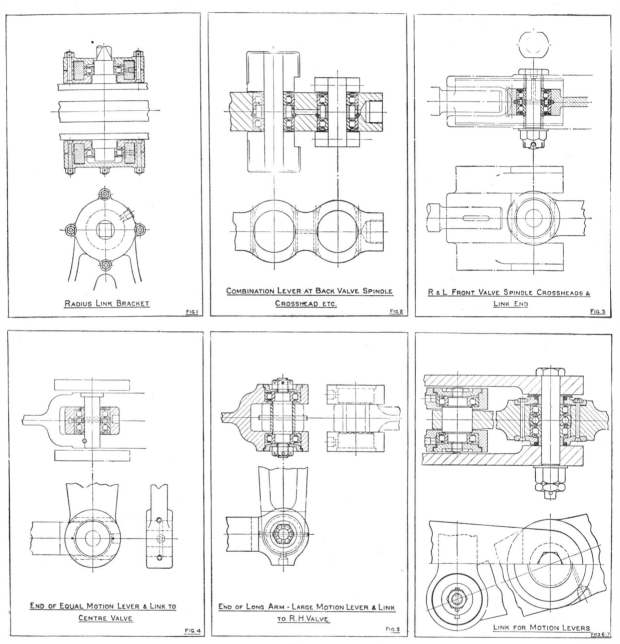

RADIUS LINK BRACKET   FIG.1

COMBINATION LEVER AT BACK VALVE SPINDLE
CROSSHEAD ETC.   FIG.2

R & L FRONT VALVE SPINDLE CROSSHEADS &
LINK END   FIG.3

END OF EQUAL MOTION LEVER & LINK TO
CENTRE VALVE   FIG.4

END OF LONG ARM - LARGE MOTION LEVER & LINK
TO R.H. VALVE   FIG.5

LINK FOR MOTION LEVERS   FIGS 6-7

FIG. 30.

in the case of the radius link bracket, the combination lever at the back valve spindle crosshead, the R and L front valve spindle crossheads and link end, further at the end of the equal motion-lever and the link to centre valve, the end of the long-arm, large motion-lever and link to right-hand valve, and the link of the motion-lever. Each of these bearings consists of two roller bearings which have a lip in the outer race abutting against a suitable shoulder or directly against an end cover. In such cases in which the two rows of rollers are mounted into one single housing, a distance ferrule serves for the proper spacing of the bearings.

The pivotal bearing of the large motion-lever and the bearing for the motion-lever link are subjected to considerable axial loads in addition to the radial or journal loads. These two bearings include, therefore, a special ball thrust bearing of the notchless deep groove type. The radial loads are taken up by two roller bearings, the races of which are not provided with lips, the location of the bearing being effected by the ball-bearing. The latter, therefore, takes care of the weight of the lever, which turns round a vertical pin.

The roller bearings referred to are fitted with nipples for the reception of grease guns, the replenishment of the grease being carried out at considerably longer intervals than are usual when oil lubrication is employed. The cost of lubrication and maintenance is therefore reduced to a minimum.

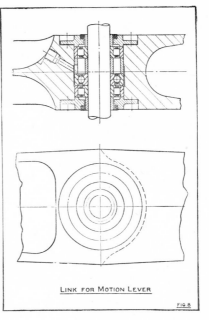

LINK FOR MOTION LEVER

FIG. 8

FIG. 30.

Special Steel for Coupling and Connecting Rods.

As the forces set up by revolving and reciprocating parts are proportional to their weight multiplied by the square of the speed, it is quite evident that with increased size and speed it tends to make the problem more difficult: (1) There is the physical difficulty owing to lack of space in introducing into the system sufficient balancing mass, and (2) a point may be reached where, on account of the speed, the unbalanced force, however carefully distributed, may exceed the maximum allowable by strain of safety and efficiency. Both these difficulties may be alleviated if the weight of the reciprocating and revolving parts is reduced by judicious use of special steels giving physical properties superior to those given by traditional materials. For many years it has been customary to use a standard steel for these details of 32-38 tons tensile strength, but now it is possible to effect a substantial reduction in the weight of these parts by suitable modification of section and the use of steels which give without loss of ductility higher tensile and fatigue properties.

Many steels have been developed to give increased maximum stress and fatigue values whilst retaining good ductility, by the addition of various alloy elements, and although some such metals may be unsuitable for the purpose under discussion, many are, provided they meet the following essentials:

1. The steel must be capable of giving consistently good physical properties throughout the mass. Certain types of steel alloy, while giving excellent tests in small sections, fail, on quenching, to harden throughout the mass, where thicker sections are involved.

2. The steel must be capable of being machined to a good finish in the heat-treated condition.

3. The question of straightness of coupling and connecting rods is one of prime importance. Steel with high tensile elastic limit, if straightened cold, tend to retain internal stresses, and it is therefore necessary to straighten hot to about 600° C., or to stabilize by heating to 600° C. after straightening. This precludes the use of any steels which suffer from temperature brittleness if air-cooled from such a temperature.

Two steels which meet these conditions are now being much used for these purposes—one a manganese molybdenum steel to give 40-45 tons tensile ("Tormanc" special steel), and the other a nickel-chrome molybdenum steel to give 55-65 tons tensile in the heat-treated condition ("Tormol" steel). For a saving of 25 per cent. in the weight of reciprocating parts by the use of these special steels this may be translated into a substantial increase in the maximum permissible speed of a locomotive.

CHAPTER V

Framing—Axle-boxes—Springs—Wheels and Tyres—Crank-axles—Balancing—Bogies—Bissel Trucks—Running Gear—Buffers—Sanding-gear, etc.

Framing.

THE framing of British built locomotives is almost invariably formed of slabs of steel plate, 1 in. to $1\frac{1}{2}$ in. thick. In America they have been universally built up of heavy bar from 4 in. to 5 in. square, and on some Colonial railways this construction is adopted; now many of the heavy locomotives in the U.S.A. have the framing of cast steel, with cylinders cast integral. These differing forms necessarily cause very divergent methods of providing for the axle-boxes, springs, gear, etc. In British locomotives the gap in the frames for accommodating the axles is fitted with heavy guides, known as " horns," or " cheeks," riveted to the plate, and in these the axle-boxes slide. In the American system, " pedestals " are forged into the bars of the frames, or cast with other members in a solid unit, as mentioned.

The plate-framed engine will naturally be the more rigid in a vertical direction, and the bar-framed engine is, therefore, claimed to be the best for the roads which are not so well laid and kept as they are in England. Another point frequently urged is that repairs to broken parts are easier to carry out in bar-framed engines, as, being usually built up of sections bolted or riveted together, if one piece gets broken or distorted another can be put in to replace it, whereas if the frames of a plate-built engine are damaged the whole has generally to be stripped before good repairs can be carried out. Against this argument, however, we have the fact that in plate-framed engines, when the damage is local and easily accessible, it is often possible to put on a patch, or otherwise make good the damage in a comparatively short space of time.

In engines having plate-frames, the main sections are made of steel plates about 1 in. thick, rolled accurately to a uniform thickness, as they are usually not machined on the sides. They will, when in position, reach from end to end of the engine, and various parts will be attached to them. The cylinders, if the engine is of the " inside " type, will be placed between them and firmly bolted to both frames. If, however, the engine has " outside " cylinders, each cylinder will necessarily be fixed to one frame only. In the first case, the cylinders form a very strong stay in themselves and prevent any " racking " of the frames, but in the second case a strong stay will have to be put between the frames at this point to support them against the alternating pull and push of the various parts of the motion. The contour of the frame will, of course, vary with different classes of engines, but the general procedure in preparing them for the pits will be similar in all cases. Taking as an instance a o–6–o type goods engine, the successive operations will be somewhat as follows: Except in the case of a new type, or an experimental engine, locomotives are rarely built as single units, it being obviously much more economical to build a series of, say, ten at a time than one alone. It will therefore be assumed that the goods engine is one of ten similar engines put in hand in rotation. Twenty main frames will thus be required, and these

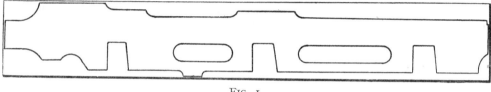

FIG. 1.

will be procured from the manufacturer, rolled truly to a suitable thickness and cut to size, but *not* to shape. The quality of metal will have been specified and tests made on pieces cut from the plates after delivery, in order to see that they are to the required specification.

Each plate will be marked off for punching out to shape. A templet of the exact outline of frame required will be used and a line marked out, as shown in Fig. 1, to guide the subsequent operations. If the frames are to be machined the plate is next taken to a punching-machine, and a succession of holes overlapping each other punched outside the line, leaving a margin all round of about $\frac{1}{4}$ in., which is afterwards removed in a slotting-machine. A portion of a frame is shown on an enlarged scale in Fig. 2, which illustrates how the outline of the frame has been followed. After being punched out in the manner described the plates are annealed, in order to counteract any straining of the material caused by the operation of punching. They are then slotted to correct form and drilled, a number being dealt with in one block (see Fig. 3). Another, and more modern method of producing frame-plates is by cutting them to shape with the oxy-acetylene jet.

Erecting Frames.

An ingenious system of erecting locomotive frames is given in Fig. 4, and the following outlines the procedure adopted. At floor-level a cast-iron base is made in sections on a concrete foundation and each section set end to end, as well as crosswise, and adjusted to a 3000th part of an inch. On these base-plates are placed " cradles," or " jigs," on which the main frames (having had the necessary pieces slotted, or cut out,

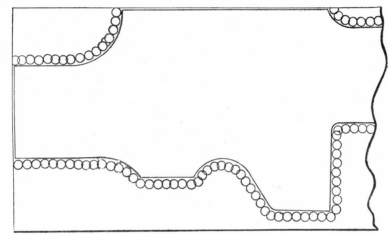

FIG. 2.

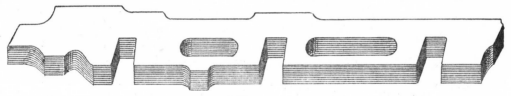

FIG. 3.

for the " horns ") are fixed. The frames are placed upside down in the jigs and set parallel to each other by means of a special distance-gauge engaged between the end of the frame and a vertical base-stand—fitted with adjustable set bolts for end fitting. The cradles are fitted with set bolts, so that the frames can be adjusted parallel through to the facing plate inserts, then held in position by securing bolts in the sides of the cradles.

The cast-steel horns are next fitted, to which the bronze liners are temporarily bolted as shown in Fig. 4. Light adjustable carrying jigs are fitted, and straight-edges are placed across the frames between the horn-plates, bronze wedges being placed by hand pressure between the straight-edges and the edge of the gauge.

A "feeler" is inserted between the inside of the cheek-plates and straight-edge, to see if the faces of the cheek-plates are perfectly parallel,

FIG. 4.—ERECTING MAIN FRAMES OF "KING" CLASS LOCOMOTIVE AT SWINDON WORKS, GREAT WESTERN RAILWAY.

FIG. 5.—FITTING AXLE-BOXES IN POSITION ON LOCOMOTIVE FRAME.

and, if not, the bronze liners are scraped. From small carrying brackets, suspended from the top of the frames, a measuring rod is placed alongside the frame between the cheek-plates from the leading to driving wheel opening, and also driving to trailing.

When the frames are dead parallel and square, the axle-boxes are next put into position and fitted with extreme accuracy. Fig. 5 shows such operation in progress. The axle-boxes are raised and lowered by three small swinging wall cranes having running pulley-blocks. In this way the men stand up to the work and are placed to the best advantage. Fig. 6 gives a general view of the frame of a 4-6-2 locomotive in the Crewe Works of L. M. & S. Railway.

This method of erection will, doubtless, in development, include the stretcher plates, cross-ties, etc., being put into position, and possibly the cylinders, so that when the engine frame goes to the erecting shop all that will remain to be done will be putting it on its wheels and then

FIG. 6.—GENERAL VIEW OF THE FRAME OF A 4–6–2 LOCOMOTIVE. L. M. & S. RAILWAY.

introducing the boiler, with its fire-box, attaching the cab, fitting the valve-gear, side-rods and details.

In the case of plate-framing, the two main slabs are connected together at the extreme front by a buffer beam, and similarly at the back with a draw-box, or framing, for the tender connection. In between cross-stays are arranged to provide the necessary lateral stiffness and secure retention of the correct alignment of the frame-plates.

The outline of the framing can be clearly followed in the drawing of the locomotive depicted in the frontispiece. Immediately behind the buffer beam, the cylinder casting, with the inside cylinders and bogie support, forms a strong and rigid connection between the side-frames. Close in front of the fire-box another cross-stay is arranged, whilst the motion-plate midway between this and the cylinders also act as retaining stiffeners.

Horn-blocks, or Cheeks.

The cheeks, Fig. 7, generally steel castings with removable and adjustable faces, are firmly riveted, or bolted, to the frames, and it is

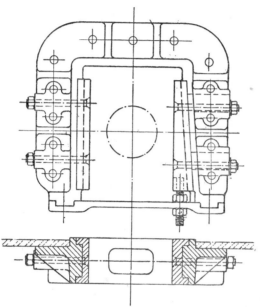

inside these that the axle-boxes freely slide up and down. The lower extremities of the cheek-blocks are tied together by "stays," to prevent any tendency to spread or open. The axle-boxes are heavy, rectangular details of iron, steel or gun-metal, designed with sliding surfaces in a wide recess, to work up and down between the faces of the horn-blocks. The flanges keep the axle-box from moving laterally more than a small allowance of a fraction of an inch.

FIG. 7.—HORN-BLOCKS

Axle-boxes.

In the cases of axle-boxes of steel or wrought iron, they have gun-metal "brasses" firmly held in the body of the box, and bored out to take the journal. These brasses usually have soft white metal alloy run into recesses arranged in them to reduce friction and protect the journal, or the brass, should overheating occur. In the latter event the white metal alloy melts out at a comparatively low temperature, and so prevents the journal of the axle from being badly scored. The top of the axle-box forms an oil reservoir for lubrication of the axle, and at the bottom is closed by a "keep," a casting of iron or steel, which forms a retaining reservoir for oil. Inside this "keep" a lubricating pad composed of worsted, etc., is maintained in contact with the journal, so that effective distribution of the lubricant is assured.

With engines having underhung springs—that is to say, with the springs below the axle-boxes (Fig. 9)—the "keep" may be secured to the axle-box by a pin (*a*) sufficiently strong to take an eye-bolt (*b*) connected to the spring, which, in turn, has supporting links (*ee*), forming the necessary attachments between the eyes (*dd*) and the brackets (*ff*) on the engine frame.

This arrangement has the merit of great simplicity, but it also has the defect that there is no means of adjusting the weight borne by that particular spring; the only method of effecting an adjustment is by removing the spring and substituting another having more or less camber to increase or diminish the load borne by the wheel, as may be desired.

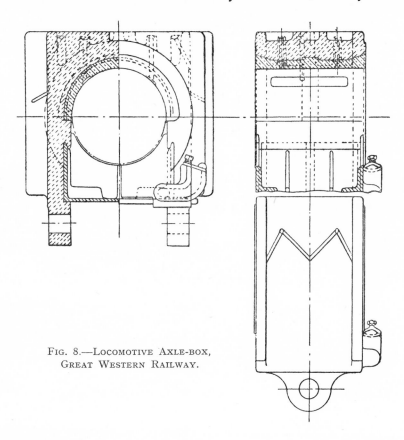

FIG. 8.—LOCOMOTIVE AXLE-BOX,
GREAT WESTERN RAILWAY.

Spring Hangers.

The simple form of hanger much used shown in Fig. 9, has the spring hung from it by a transverse pin (*a*) passing through the lower portion of the axle box and keep. Two links form the attachments between the eyes of the spring and the frame brackets as already noted.

A modification is sometimes used in which the spring links are attached to the spring ends by means of pins, but at the upper end are extended and made round in section and provided with screw-threads on which nuts are placed. The brackets on the frame are modified accordingly, with holes through which the hangers pass, the nuts giving the necessary bearing. This modified form of hanger allows of adjustment by means of the nuts, which can be moved up or down the hangers and so alter the pressure upon the spring, as needed.   The nuts are usually provided with loose washers above them, which are formed with ribs across their upper faces, these engaging in suitable curved depressions formed in the spring brackets, thus forming " knife-edge " bearings to allow of the movement of the spring hangers when the spring lengthens or shortens as the load varies with the inequalities of the road.   Sometimes the loose washers are dispensed with and the upper faces of the nuts provided with raised ribs, which have the additional effect of preventing the nuts from slacking; in the other case, two nuts are advisable on each hanger, one to act as a lock nut.   The ends of the spring hangers are generally made long enough to project above the brackets, and a cotter is driven through the projecting portion to prevent the risk of accident should any of the spring gear fail.

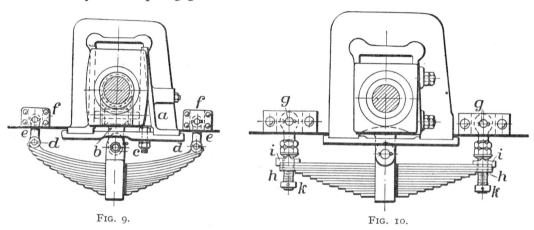

FIG. 9.   FIG. 10.

A customary continental variation of this method of hanging the spring is shown in Fig. 10, the attachment of the hangers being reversed. Thus the hangers are attached to the frame brackets by means of pins at *gg* and the shanks pass through suitable holes cut in the spring-plates at *hh*.   The spring is provided with wearing-plates at *ii*, formed with knife-edges, and on these either the nuts or loose washers take their bearings.   It will be noticed that collars *kk* are secured to the lower ends of the hangers to prevent the spring from falling in the event of one hanger giving way.

The gears so far described are arranged so as to have the hangers in compression, but most designers prefer to have them in tension, because in that case springs have more freedom and can " centre " themselves, and thus allow the axle-boxes to move more easily in their guides.   To secure this—in the case of underhung springs—it is usual to use longer brackets, as shown in Fig. 11.   In the method here shown several modifications are apparent. The pins to secure the hangers to the springs are dispensed with, the hangers being made in the form of a loop working over the spring end, which is shaped with a transverse

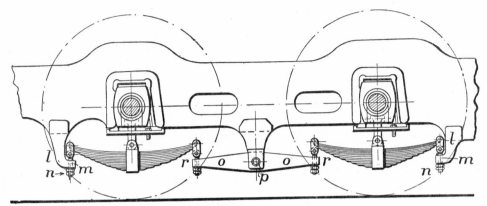

FIG. 11.—ARRANGEMENT OF UNDERHUNG SPRINGS.

bead or thickening for that purpose. The hangers are relatively short, links and additional hanger bolts are provided, as *mm*, which pass through the brackets and are adjusted by nuts *nn*. The play of the springs is taken by the links.

When the springs are above the axle-box, then connection is made through a support resting on the top of it and connected to the under side of the buckle of the spring, as illustrated in Fig. 12, where a "claw" lever is shown pulling the end of the spring down to enable the coupling pin to be inserted. The springs reduce the shocks transferred from the wheels when running, and may be of different forms — laminated, plate, spiral, or volute. The first named are usually constructed of the best spring

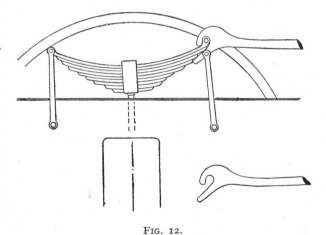

FIG. 12.

steel, with plates about 5 in. wide by $\frac{1}{2}$ in. thick, the number varying with the load to be carried. They are held together by a band, or "spring-buckle," and it is to this that the spring-pillar, or support, from the axle-box imparts its movement. The bulk of the weight of the engine is carried on the springs, and is termed "spring-borne," but there must be a considerable percentage, consisting of the wheels, axles, etc., which is not resting on the wheels, accounting for considerable dead-weight on the rails; it is obvious that the lighter these details can be made consistent with proper strength, the better.

Equalizing Beams.

As all the axle-boxes fitted with independent springs are permanently loaded with the full weight to be carried by them, it follows that as the wheels pass over inequalities in the rails the weight per axle may be largely increased at certain periods, therefore, many engines have two or more pairs of wheels fitted with compensating, or equalizing beams, so that the raising and falling of the wheels (as mentioned) may be suitably accommodated without causing undue load on any one axle-box. These remarks particularly apply to locomotives intended for rough tracks.

The general arrangement is clearly seen in Fig. 11, where the equalizing beam O is pivoted centrally at P in a bracket fixed to the frame. The adjacent ends of the two springs are attached to the ends of the beam at RR, with links and eye-bolts, in the same way as they are supported at the other end by the brackets L; the eye-bolts M, with the nuts N, give ready means for adjustment.

The equalizing system is carried out to a much greater extent in foreign practice than in British; in fact, some locomotive engineers in this country consider that equalizing has a tendency to make an engine roll and pitch when running at high speeds, and that it is unnecessary on a well-constructed and carefully maintained track.

Wheel-centres.

The centres, or bodies, of wheels are now invariably of steel castings, and much ingenuity is shown in the design of these so as to secure spokes, rim, etc., as light as possible, yet rigid and stiff. The boss of the wheel has to be large enough to safely withstand the strain due to the axle being pressed in and securely held. For coupling wheels, this boss is extended to receive the coupling rod and crankpin, and, of course, in the case of drivers, the driving crankpin. The number of spokes radiating from the boss to the rim must necessarily depend on the size of the wheel. They are usually taper, and the section varies from an ellipse to a rectangle, with rounded corners. The hole for the reception of the axle is bored out, and the ends of the axle turned to such dimensions as are needed for these parts to be forced together. The hole may be parallel or slightly taper, and the axle is then forced in, whilst cold, under hydraulic pressure—generally specified as from 10 to 12 tons per in. diameter of the wheel seat. This pressing in is performed in a machine having an automatic recording apparatus attached to it, so that records can be kept for any future reference required.

Coupled wheels are generally additionally secured with a steel key of rectangular section inserted in a key-way formed half in the boss of the wheel and half in the wheel seat of the axle. For bogie carrying or tender wheels this key is usually absent, being considered unnecessary.

Tyre Fastenings.

The tyres encircling the wheel-centres being subject to heavy wear are of hard steel rolled from a solid ingot, so that no weld or joint is required. As they are shrunk to the wheel-centres, the steel is of high tenacity. There are many devices for securing the tyres to the wheel-centres of a locomotive. A secure fastening is necessary to withstand the stresses from oscillation and the passage of curves at high speeds, when the weight of the vehicle is thrown against the outer rail by the flanges on that side; further, there is the need for precautions against flaws and broken tyres, and also the necessity to counteract the action of the brakes, which, at times, sets up very severe stresses.

In early days a common fastening was by means of set-screws, or studs, screwed through the rim of the wheel-centre into the tyre. This was simple and efficient so long as the tyre remained intact, but it did not provide a *continuous* fastening, which is the object of more refined arrangements. (4), (5) and (6), Fig. 13, show such fastenings. The tyre was first shrunk on to the centre, and the holes then drilled through the rim into the tyre, tapped, and the screws put in a tight fit.

One of the earliest fastenings is: (1) in this the iron tyre was shrunk on and then secured to the rim of the wheel-centre by six or eight tapered bolts passing through the two and fastened with nuts, as shown. The bolt was turned to a taper of 1 in 8 for a length of 2 in., and after the nuts had been well screwed up the bolts were riveted over. The fastening, apart from being non-continuous, was not satisfactory, as it caused the tyres to wear unevenly; if the bolts were harder than the metal of the tyre they would wear less rapidly and cause lumps, and vice versa.

(2) shows a fastening which would not prove very substantial for present-day use, but it represents an original attempt at securing a " continuous " interlocking of rim and tyre. In this design the tyre was recessed to a depth of $\frac{1}{4}$ in. all round, leaving a lip on both sides,

the inside of these faces being tapered $\frac{1}{8}$ in. The wheel-centre was turned to a diameter equal to the bore of the recess, with edges of similar taper, but $\frac{1}{4}$ in. less in total width, to permit of the centre being readily adjusted in position. When shrunk on and gauged, molten zinc was run into the recesses and the fastening completed. Some British railways used this method for engine and tender wheels.

Another arrangement shown at (3) was also much used in the days of iron tyres. A flange (indicated by dotted lines) was left on the tyre,

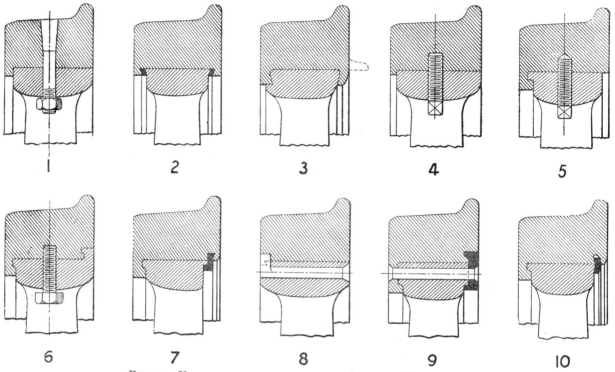

FIG. 13.—VARIOUS METHODS OF FASTENING TYRES TO WHEEL-CENTRES.

and after the wheel-centre had been put into position this was hammered over, as shown. There was not much risk of the tyre coming off, but whenever the wheel-centre required removing, the flange had to be cut away, thereby destroying the tyre.

(7) illustrates a fastening by means of a continuous retaining ring. Here the tyre has a groove $\frac{1}{2}$ in. wide and 5/16 in. deep, turned level with the outside edge of the rim of the wheel, into which is sprung a steel ring of the section shown; the ring beds over a lip turned on the wheel. After the wheel-centre and retaining ring are in position the outer edge of the tyre is hammered over. This fastening, although very satisfactory, has the disadvantage that it cannot be renewed in its entirety.

When a tyre is replaced, only segments can be introduced, which discounts the arrangement as an efficient continuous fastening.

Rivets are used to secure the tyre (8) with heads of a special shape which engage in slots in the rim and tyre. The heads are $\frac{3}{8}$ in. deep and $\frac{7}{8}$ in. wide. It will be seen that the tyre cannot come off, owing to the lip on the inner edge of the tyre and the rivets; this is a simple fastening, but it cannot be looked upon as continuous.

Another fastening is illustrated at (9) of a tyre equipped with a loose retaining ring riveted on to the rim of the wheel and the tyre. The tyre is turned with a lip, or flange, on the inner side, deep enough to receive the rivets; after the centre has been put into place the retaining ring is adjusted and the whole riveted together. This is an excellent fastening and has been largely adopted. It possesses all the advantages of a continuous fastening, can be readily removed or replaced, and holds wheel and tyre well together to resist loosening by the action of the brakes.

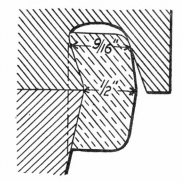

FIG. 14.—DETAIL OF RETAINING RING.

The last sketch (10) gives a different form of fastening by means of a continuous retaining ring. The ring is tapered in section, where it fits into the groove round the tyre so that hammering down the edge in sections holds the ring and prevents it from turning. The tapered section is reduced at these points to assist. An enlarged section of the ring is given in Fig. 14. The tyre can be removed by turning out the ring, and neither centre nor tyre suffers from the operation.

Axles.

The axles are of steel, straight for the carrying wheels, the driving wheels of outside cylindered engines, or coupled wheels of others; they are cranked for the driving wheels of inside cylindered engines.

Crank-axles.

Crank-axles are either complicated forgings, or are built up of separate pieces very accurately machined and screwed or shrunk together. Safety bands are provided to strengthen the crank webs, and these are shrunk on, as represented in Fig. 15, which also shows extensions to the webs, to act as counterbalance weights to the revolving crankpin and its attachments. The building up of crank-axles has much to recommend it, as in forging such details, objectionable corners may be left, becoming forerunners of fracture and ultimate breakage. Fig. 16 shows the ingenious construction of the built-up crank-axle used for the compound four-cylinder locomotive, No. 10,000, for the L. & N.E. Railway.

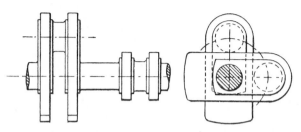

FIG. 15.—STROUDLEY CRANK-AXLE.

Balancing.

In the interests of smooth travel, saving in wear and tear of running gear, tyres, etc., it is essential that the revolving masses and as much of the reciprocating weights as possible should be balanced. Considerable care is devoted to this, but, roughly, it may be taken that all the revolving, and up to about two-thirds of the reciprocating, weights are balanced. For this purpose, pockets, or receptacles, are formed between the spokes of the driving wheels which can be filled with lead to the required extent, or weights cast in the rim, to counterbalance the forces set up by the rapid revolutions and movements of the motion and running gear.

Wheels of moderately large diameter are much easier to deal with than small ones, but as these latter are generally under slow-moving locomotives, their comparatively un-balanced state is not of so much importance.

Three- and four-cylin-dered engines are fairly

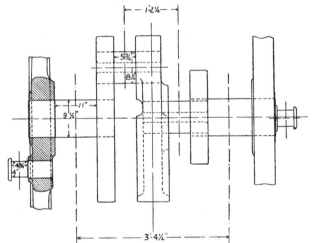

FIG. 16.—CRANK-AXLE OF LOCOMOTIVE NO. 10,000, L. & N.E. RAILWAY.

easy to balance, owing to the disposition of the driving cranks—in fact, in the locomotive shown in the frontispiece the balancing is almost perfect, and very steady running is assured.

In engines with two outside cylinders, the balance weights are located almost exactly opposite the crankpins, as the power is applied, approximately, in the plane of the wheel, and the disturbing influence of one crank is not felt to any extent by the other.

In engines with inside cylinders the balance weights are usually placed to one side of the centre line of the axle and crankpin, on account of the power being applied away from the plane of the wheel. If the weight were placed opposite, it would not correctly balance, as the other crank at right angles influences it.

Bogies.

The front of the express engine illustrated (frontispiece) is carried on a four-wheeled truck, or bogie. The connection between this and the main frame of the engine is through the pivot, or centre pin, about which the bogie can swivel. The frames of the bogie are quite independent of the framing of the engine. Horn-blocks are provided for the axle-boxes, so that these can move up and down, similar to those of the engine. The pivot casting forms a substantial transverse stay for the bogie framing, and the casting above equally consolidates the engine. The lateral movement allowed between the top plate and the surface of the bogie casting may be from 1 in. to $1\frac{1}{2}$ in.—in fact, in some cases more. The provision of a bogie truck gives the engine a deal of flexibility, and also distributes the weight of the leading end over two axles instead of one.

A drawing is given in Fig. 17 of another arrangement of bogie truck wherein two springs of the laminated type are employed, one on each side of the frame, supported by suitable bearing-brackets. An equalizing beam formed of two plates encloses each spring, and this has a bearing on the top of each axle-box, and is attached to the ends of the spring by links; the link-pins form an additional stay to the equalizing beam by holding its two plates together and stiffening the arrangement. The lateral movement is controlled by two laminated springs placed across the frame, as is clearly shown in the drawing.

There are numerous other forms of bogie truck in use, but all designed for similar objects, viz. securing a flexible and easy wheel-base for the engine, with a satisfactory distribution of weight on the track.

If the rigid wheel-base of an engine is too long, the flanges of the end wheels will certainly grind between the rails on sharp curves, and this difficulty is met by the lateral allowance of the bogie mentioned. In some cases a truck with only one pair of wheels is used, Fig. 18. This is known as a " bissel," from the name of the engineer who originated it. In this the pivot on which the frame carrying the two wheels can oscillate is fixed behind the centre line of the axle. The portion of the weight of the engine on the truck is usually carried by links which swing laterally from a cross-beam attached to the body of the truck.

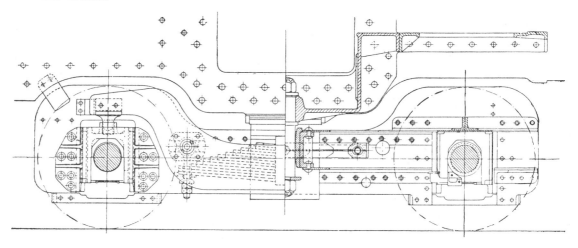

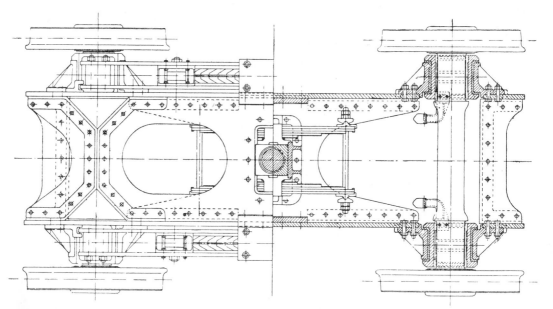

FIG. 17.—LEADING BOGIE WITH LAMINATED SPRING CONTROL.

Radial Axle-boxes.

There are many forms of radial axle-boxes in use; the one illustrated in Fig. 19 represents a type which has had considerable adoption. It is shown as applied to a locomotive with a long wheel-base for the 2 ft. 6 in. gauge, and intended to operate round comparatively sharp

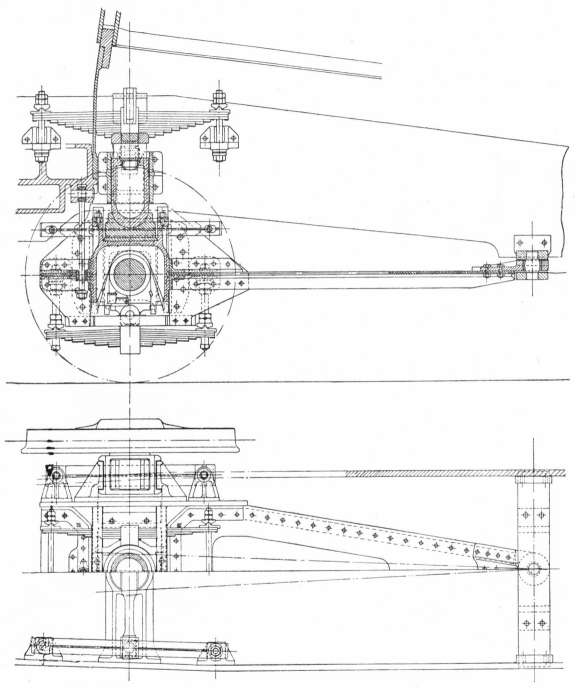

FIG. 18.—TRAILING BISSEL TRUCK WITH CENTRAL PIVOT.

curves. The steel axle-boxes are machined with curved faces, which tend to secure easy traverse. The gun-metal bearings have steel slippers, or packing-pieces, also machined, with convex upper surfaces, which enable them to be readily removed for examination. The inclined

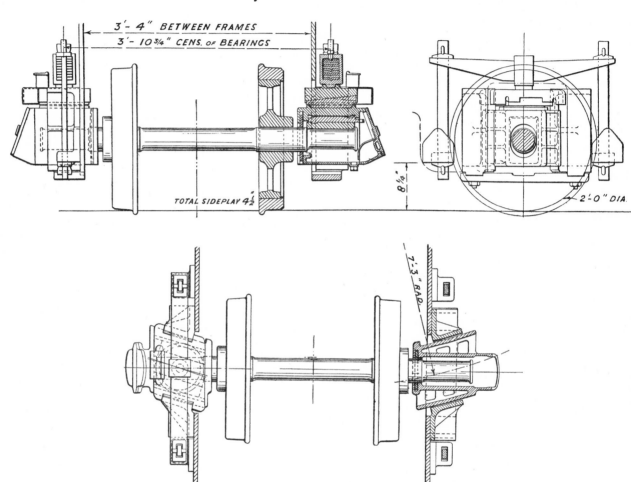

FIG. 19.—CORTAZZI TRAILING TRUCK OF GWALIOR LIGHT RAILWAYS LOCOMOTIVE.

planes of the slippers ensure the engine returning to its central position after a curve has been taken.

The buffers at the leading end consist of cylindrical forgings in which plungers are placed, held in position by rods passing through the buffer socket and supported inside either by volute springs of steel or rubber cushions. The draw-hook has a stem passing through the buffer beam, and behind the latter either volute springs or rubbers, as in the buffers. The connection used for coupling the engine to the tender will be described when dealing with tenders in a following chapter.

At the front of the framing, or attached direct to the bogie, are guard-irons, to remove obstructions from the rails. On American, Indian, or South African, as well as other Colonial railways, a "cow-catcher," or pilot, is fitted. This is generally fixed to the main cross-frame, or "bumper," as being better able to receive and withstand shocks.

Brake Gear.

All engines—either tender or tank—are provided with brake gear, Fig. 20, arranged to work by power, the latter being steam, air, or vacuum.

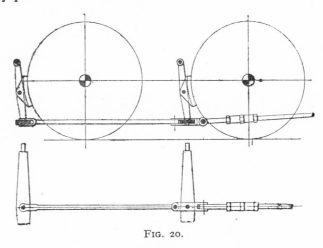

FIG. 20.

Steam fitments for the engine and tender are much used in connection with automatic vacuum brakes for the train, and hand-gear is also often provided for the engine, and always for the tender.

Brake hangers are provided at each wheel, on which blocks are suspended for operating on the tyres. The most approved system clasps the wheels; that is to say, there is a brake-block on either side of each wheel, which tends to keep them in correct position and relieve strains on the bearings when the brakes are applied.

Sand-gear.

Another important adjunct must be mentioned, and that is the device used for sanding the rails when the engine is starting or when the rails are greasy. Sand-boxes are provided on the platform of the engine (see frontispiece), or below it, and these have pipes to convey the sand to the front of the driving wheels; in tank engines, front and rear. Latterly, steam- or air-jets have been employed to drive the sand more effectively under the treads of the wheels, but for these dried sand has had to be used, and to secure this furnaces are usually installed at locomotive depots. Despite the best of precautions being taken to obtain the driest sand, it will, at times, be blown from the required point of contact; and there is always the tendency to "clog" in damp weather. In the device illustrated, the fact that sand has an affinity for water has been made use of, and a mixture of sand and water is deposited on the rail, obviating the necessity for drying to secure efficient delivery of the grit at the required spot. Fig. 21 shows the arrangement of apparatus applied to a 0–4–4 tank locomotive requiring sand for both directions of running. A is the water-valve receiving its supply from the boiler, which is then directed by the distributing valve B to either the front or back sand-boxes. Any drip is removed by the connection C, and also from the lower side of the steam-valve. DD are the sanders, of which a large sectional view, Fig. 22, is given to

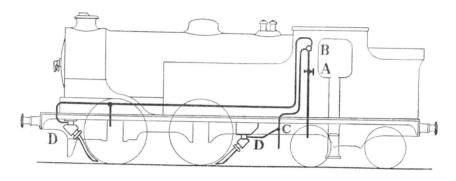

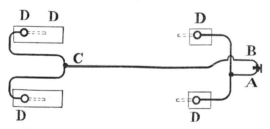

FIG. 21.—DIAGRAM OF CONNECTIONS, WET SANDING APPARATUS.

better illustrate their construction and operation. Water entering at the point shown is distributed to the nozzles in the sand-box from the upper chamber, and this causes an emulsion of sand to be formed which passes from the strainer to the sanding pipe. An adjustable screen is fitted, which enables the outlet to be regulated according to the grade of sand used, whilst a ridge effectually prevents the sand at the bottom of the slope falling into the sand-box, until forced by the jet of water. The small nozzle for water will be noted, which, being in direct contact with moist sand resting on the ledge, ensures instantaneous emission into the pipe when the water-valve is opened.

Modern signalling arrangements based on electrical contacts with the rails require that either the supply of sand shall be minimized or provision made for cleansing the rails after passage of the engine to ensure satisfactory conductivity.

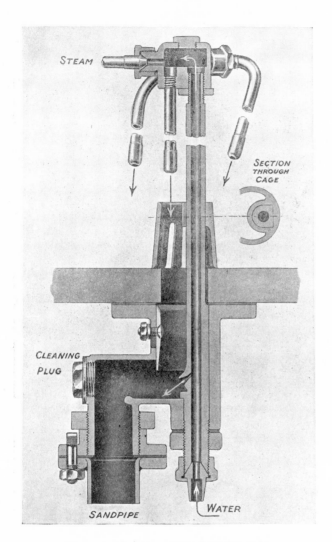

FIG. 22.—LAMBERT WET SANDING-GEAR.

Cab.

The cab provided to afford protection to the engine crew from inclement weather and climatic conditions assumes very different patterns and proportions on the various railroads. From the plain piece of plate used, termed a " weather-board," fitted to early locomotives, much more comfortable and practical shelters have been developed. That on the engine shown in the frontispiece offers all the protection men should require in the temperate British climate, but on foreign and colonial railways, where more severe conditions are met with, larger and more commodious cabs are often provided.

A wooden platform will be noticed arranged over the footplate, which forms a comfortable non-conductor floor of convenient height for the enginemen.   In tropical countries the roofs of cabs are usually made

FIG. 23.—INTERIOR OF CAB, SHOWING POSITIONS OF FITTINGS.

double, and of wood, with some non-conducting substance between; further, a second cab to interlock with that on the engine is often fitted to the front of the tender, ample protection from the sun being very necessary.   Nearly all the operating handles, controls, etc., are now placed in the cab of a locomotive, and much ingenuity is displayed in the arrangement of the numerous handles, etc.   The accompanying illustration, Fig. 23, of the interior of a modern cab is interesting, and careful study will show how convenient everything is placed for the manipulation by the driver and fireman.

CHAPTER VI

Lubrication—Axle-boxes—Bearings—Motion—Oil and Grease arrangements—Sight-feed
Mechanical Lubricators, etc.

Lubrication, General.

It is of the greatest importance that all the surfaces exposed to friction, joints, etc., are well lubricated, as the relative speeds between them are usually high. The frictional resistance of two surfaces running in a bath of oil, as some axle journals do, is nearly independent of the pressure between, unless this should be excessive and the lubricant squeezed out. With dry surfaces the friction would be proportional to the pressure between them, but the conditions existing in a modern locomotive are something between these two extremes. When an engine is starting and at very low speed the lubrication is not so effective, and the conditions approach somewhat that of dry surfaces. At high speeds, however, with efficient lubrication, the conditions resemble those of a journal running in an oil-bath. In bearings which are well lubricated, the oil forms a film between the moving surfaces to prevent metallic contact between them, and the frictional resistance depends chiefly upon that offered in the disintegration of the film. Friction, therefore, does not depend so much on the load on the bearings as on the thickness, area, and viscosity of the lubricating film involved. The viscosity depends on the nature of the lubricant, its temperature, and its gravity.

If a film of oil or lubricant of sufficient thickness could always be maintained between a bearing and the surface of a revolving journal, or moving detail, the materials of which the working surfaces are made would not, perhaps, be of much importance. At low speeds, when starting, for instance, or if the temperature rises to such an extent that the viscosity of the lubricant is lowered, the oil film may be squeezed out and the metals allowed to come into actual contact. A journal *well greased* will move from " rest " more easily than one lubricated with oil, for the reason that grease is not so easily squeezed out as oil is, and there is no doubt that the use of suitable heavy grease for lubricating the bearings of locomotives, as will be mentioned later, is rapidly increasing.

If the sides of a brass are cut away to reduce the arc of contact, frictional resistance will be reduced, but this procedure must not be allowed to reduce the bearing area too much, or it will tend to assist in causing the lubricant to be squeezed out. From 200 to 300 lbs. per sq. in. may be taken as the limits for the load on a locomotive main bearing.

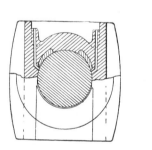

FIG. 1.

As influencing the wear of axle-box brasses, the effect of the action of the brakes must not be neglected. If brake-blocks are provided at the front of the wheels only, the tendency is to press the journal on to the back of the bearing and cause wear there, or vice versa, hence the advisability of braking both sides of wheels.

Certain types of axle-boxes used with engines having outside frames are similar to tender axle-boxes, and should have the same arrangements for lubrication provided. Fig. 1 shows a device adopted to meet the objection to oil-holes and grooves cut directly in the crown of a brass. Oil is delivered through holes AA on the "on" side of the journal, and flows round the grooves shown without waste. Two small exit grooves, BB, are made if the Journal

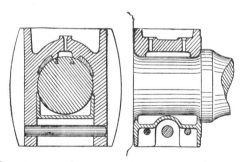

FIGS. 2 AND 3.—OIL-HOLES IN AXLE-BOXES.

is also lubricated by means of a pad, and the oil flowing through BB is returned to the reservoir below.

To avoid the introduction of oil through holes in the zone of maximum pressure, the oil should be introduced at points above the commencement of the bearing area, as shown in Fig. 2.

Many axle-boxes are supplied with oil-passages, as given in Fig. 3, but there is no standard system for this.

Oil-trimmings.

The worsted syphon trimming is general in British practice, but in American engines the needle lubricator is preferred. The trimming made by wrapping worsted strands lengthwise round a piece of twisted copper wire, should be a proper fit in the oil-hole, and the easiness of this fit can only be judged after considerable experience, for it varies with the oil used. If it be too easy, the oil will syphon away too quickly, and if too tight the oil cannot feed fast enough. The most suitable engine oil should be used; a thick cylinder oil, for instance, would soon choke up a worsted trimming, and oils which give a gummy deposit will do the same. Therefore all trimmings should be regularly examined. If water has found its way into a box and wetted the trimming, it should be changed, since a trimming soaked with water cannot syphon oil. For the same reason trimmings should be well dried before using, to remove the moisture absorbed from the atmosphere; they are then soaked in the oil with which they are to be used. A tail trimming should not be too short in the tail, or it will not reach down into the oil, when the oil reservoir has run low.

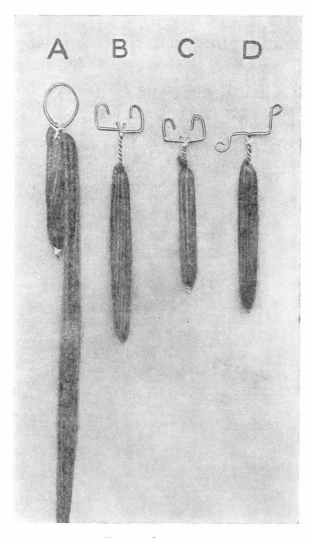

FIG. 4.—OIL-TRIMMINGS.

Fig. 4 shows samples of worsted trimmings as used in a locomotive. A is a tail trimming for a bogie axle-box; for a driving axle-box the

stem would be somewhat longer. It should be long enough to enter
the brass, so that the oil is delivered well into the oil-hole in the latter.
If the trimming comes short of this, the oil may work out along the
surface between the brass and the body of the box. B and C are ordinary
plug trimmings for a big-end and a coupling rod respectively, and their
length should be made in accordance with the same consideration as in
the case of A. The top ends of the twisted wires are bent at right
angles to rest upon the top of the oil-tube so that the trimming does not
slip down the tube. The upright ends touch the reservoir cap and
prevent the trimming from being shaken upwards as the big-end revolves.
D is a plug trimming similar to the above for an eccentric, but is provided
with a differently shaped end to suit an oil-cup with an inclined tube.

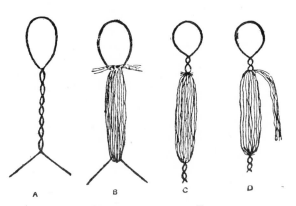 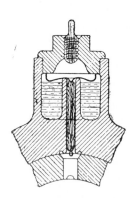
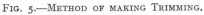

FIG. 5.—METHOD OF MAKING TRIMMING.   FIG. 5A.—PLUG TRIMMING.

The method of making a trimming is shown in Fig. 5. The copper
wire is twisted as at A, and the strands of worsted are passed round it
as shown at B, until the required size is obtained. The two ends of the
worsted are left at the top. Two or three twists are given to the copper
wire at the top and bottom to secure the worsted firmly. The ends of
the trimming are cut off as at C for a plug trimming, or D for a tail
trimming.

A plug trimming is also shown in Fig. 5A. A piece of cane or cork
is screwed into the hole in the cap of the oil reservoir. Being slightly
porous, it allows of the entry of air to replace the oil used. In cups
with a spring button a small hole is drilled through the button for the
same purpose. Unless sufficient air be admitted the syphoning action
will stop.

The syphoning or oil-lifting power of worsteds depends upon the
closeness of the material and the kind of oil used. Closely plaited
cotton wick gives a longer lift than worsted, as its capillary action is

better, and, therefore, for axle-boxes with deep oil-wells a cotton-wick trimming may be used.

Fig. 6 is a good example of the arrangements of lubrication provided for a driving axle-box. The oil receptacle is attached to the framing of the engine in such a position as to be easily accessible for attention whilst the engine is running. In the top of the bearing, brass A, a sealed space, B, is formed, and this is provided with channels, C and D, through which oil can pass to the grooves, or recess, E, in the crown of the brass.

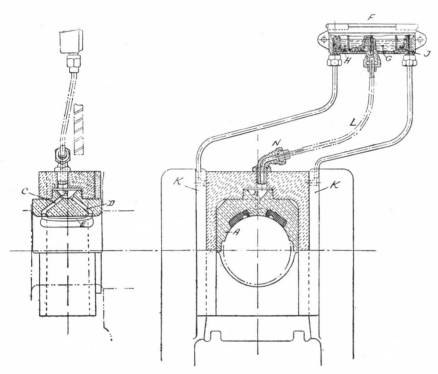

FIG. 6.—LOCOMOTIVE DRIVING AXLE-BOX.

The auxiliary oil-box F has three compartments, of which the centre and larger one, G, contains the oil for supply to the box-bearing. The end compartments, H and J, contain oil for lubricating the faces of the axle-box KK, where they slide in the horn-blocks. A flexible pipe, L, is necessary for the central connection as the axle-box moves up and down in its guides. There are no trimmings in the axle-box itself; these are conveniently located in the oil-box.

Two main differences exist in the lubrication of crankpins and that of axle-boxes. Owing to the rotation of the crankpin about a centre, the lubricating cup must be carried round with the pin, so that " plug " trimmings are used in place of " tail " trimmings. As the pressure of the piston acts alternately on each side, it causes the big-end brass to press on the opposite sides of the crankpin during each revolution— an action which is of great advantage, as the oil can enter between the brass and the pin on the slacker side, enabling a film to form during each half revolution as the pressure is transferred.   Further, this alternating pressure has the effect of partially squeezing oil from one side of the pin to the other.   At high speeds the alternating pressure is exerted for such short periods of time that the film cannot be squeezed out, though, at very low speeds, the effect may be more pronounced. From this it will be seen that a much higher bearing pressure per unit of area is permissible in crankpins than in the case of axle-box journal bearings, where the alternate variations in pressure do not occur.

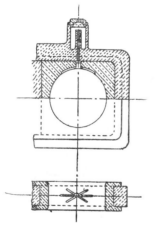

FIG. 6A.—CONNECTING ROD END LUBRICATOR.

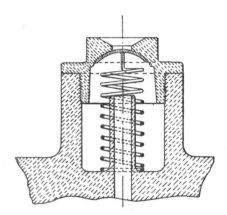

FIG. 7.—CONNECTING ROD OIL-CUP.

In British locomotives having inside cylinders the maximum pressure per square inch will vary from 1000 lbs. to 1600 lbs., or, say, an average of about 1350 lbs.; in outside cylinder engines the crankpin pressure will be slightly more, by, say, 200 lbs.

Fig. 6A shows the connecting rod end with the oil-grooves which are usually provided in the brass for the better admission of the lubricant. A detailed drawing of an oil-cup, with an internal cap held up by a spring, is shown in Fig. 7.

As will be noted by the foregoing descriptions, " tail " trimmings are used for axle-boxes, whereby oil is syphoned over to the oil-hole. Syphoning is not needed for big-ends, as their motion constantly throws the oil up; therefore a plug trimming is preferred.

Fig. 8 shows a needle lubricator where the oscillation of the needle up and down in the central hole, caused by the motion of the engine, constantly induces, or projects, oil to the bearing. The motion of the needle is controlled by the set-screw with a lock-nut in the cover. It is claimed for this method that it is very economical in oil, as the supply can be so easily adjusted. It is necessary to exercise care with needle lubricators, in order to prevent shortage of lubrication on long runs, since their behaviour is quite different in service to those having worsted plug trimmings. Of course, any fineness of adjustment of supply can be produced by introducing thinner or thicker needles, as required.

The crosshead, with its gudgeon pin, on which the smaller end of the connecting rod is carried, is another detail needing special arrangements for lubrication. Fig. 9 illustrates the method of providing oil

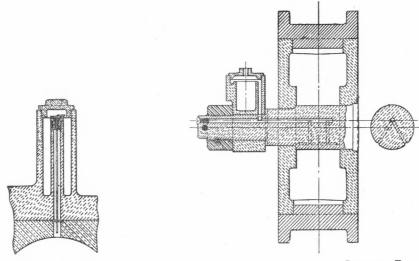

FIG. 8.—NEEDLE LUBRICATOR,
BRITISH PATTERN.

FIG. 9.—LUBRICATION OF GUDGEON PIN.

lubrication for a gudgeon pin in the crosshead of an engine having two bars—upper and lower.

Lubrication of the eccentrics requires oil-cups, with either plug trimmings or mechanical methods for ensuring the feed of oil. On an express engine running at 60 miles an hour, an eccentric sheave may have a linear speed of 25 ft. per second, and this calls for efficient lubrication. The pressure between the strap and the sheave will vary as each end receives its turn, and thus the conditions are somewhat similar to those of the big-end on the crankpin. Fig. 10 shows an oil-well on an eccentric where the sheave and strap are both of cast-iron. A piece of tube projects up into the oil-chamber, and is used for taking the plug trimming. A second oil-hole will be seen for a direct supply of oil in case of an emergency; this is usually closed with a cork.

Fig. 11 gives the details of the lubrication for the block in the expansion link of the link-motion, whilst Fig. 12 shows a slide-bar with its oil-holes.

Piston-rods need attention, and Fig. 13 gives a common method providing oil by means of a " squab " surrounding the rod, and attached to the stuffing-box, whilst Fig. 14 illustrates the manner adopted when the squab is enclosed in a suitable box on the gland.

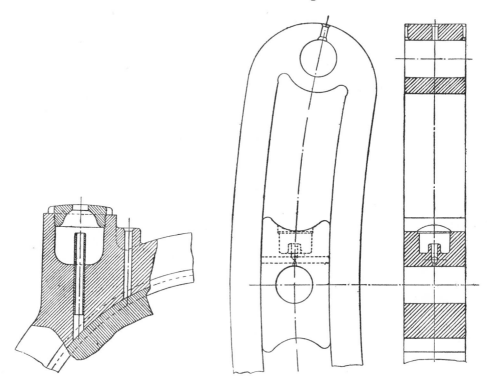

FIG. 10.—LUBRICATION OF ECCENTRIC.   FIG. 11.—LUBRICATION OF EXPANSION LINK AND BLOCK.

With the increase in size, development of power, introduction of high steam-pressure, etc., the question of lubrication of the cylinders, valves, etc., has received serious attention, and many mechanical devices are now to be found on locomotives for securing constant and regular lubrication of moving parts. These devices can be classed under two comprehensive heads: (1) Those in which the supply of oil from the lubricating device to the parts to be lubricated is assured by displacement of the oil by water or condensed steam; (2) those in which oil is forcibly introduced by mechanically operated pumps. The principle of displacement of oil by condensed steam has been applied to locomotive lubricators for many years past; the great advance in recent years has been the introduction of " sight-feed," so that the amount of oil being

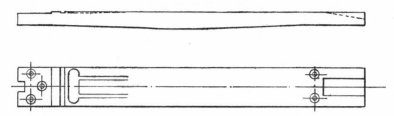

FIG. 12.—SLIDE-BAR.

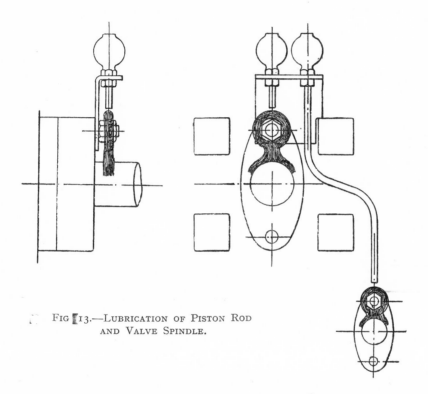

FIG. 13.—LUBRICATION OF PISTON ROD
AND VALVE SPINDLE.

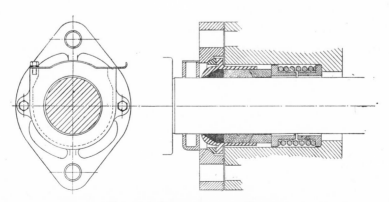

FIG. 14.—LUBRICATION OF GLAND.

fed can be *seen* and adjusted. In earlier lubricators incorporating this principle, the incoming steam and outgoing oil used the same passage and pipe. Latterly these have been separated, the steam entering by a different passage, the oil being delivered through a distinct connection. In Fig. 15 the steam regulated by the valve A enters the lubricator nearby. It is admitted to the oil reservoir by means of the pipe O, the steam is condensed in the oil reservoir J, and as it becomes water, sinks to the bottom, displacing the oil which passes down the tube P into the outlet controlled by valve E, where it is adjusted so that the oil feeds up, drip by drip, through the glass tube D. From D it passes the check-valve M, provided to prevent escape of steam through the passages should the sight-feed glass break. From here it finds its way to the delivery H, thence through the oil-pipe to the steam-chest. At N there is an auxiliary feed-valve to be utilized if the sight-feed glass breaks; it can be adjusted to permit of the same feed as given by valve E; it is kept closed during normal working. In case of the glass breaking, valve E is closed and the oil passes through a small hole Q, thence through the passages R and S to the oil outlet H.

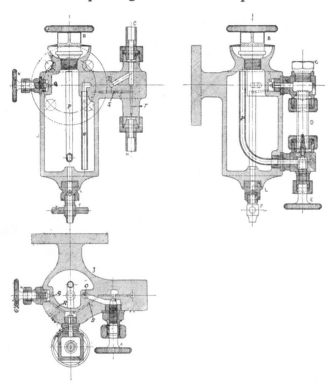

FIG. 15.—WAKEFIELD'S SIGHT-FEED LUBRICATOR.

To atomize the oil as it leaves the lubricator at H, the steam-jet T is provided. The lubricator is filled through the plug B, which must not be removed before the valve A has been closed, or hot oil will be blown out. The waste water of condensation is allowed to drain out through the orifice F, which has a removable seat in L. Such a sight-feed displacement lubricator is placed inside the cab, so as to be easily seen by the driver, who can always assure himself of the oil being fed properly.

A development of this form of lubricator is shown in Fig. 16, which

gives a double-feed arrangement.
separate coil and admitted from
this to the base of the lubricator,
then the oil displaced from the
reservoir descends through the
pipes J, and passes up through
the sight-feed glass as before,
the feed being regulated by
valves below. Check valves are
provided to automatically shut
off the pipes in case of the sight-
feed glasses breaking. The passages will be readily followed from
the figure.

To secure uniformity of the
oil-feed an ingenious device has
been introduced whereby whatever the position of the regulator
may be the oil-feed remains un-
changed. When the regulator is
moved to first position the valve
(Fig. 17) is forced on to the
seating by the difference existing
between the boiler pressure in
the lubricator and the steam-chest

In this the steam is condensed in a

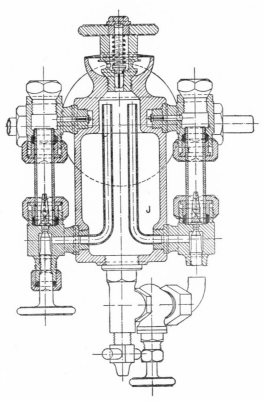

FIG. 16.—WAKEFIELD No. 2 DOUBLE-FEED
HYDROSTATIC LUBRICATOR.

pressure, which at the moment will be considerable. The oil-feed
then takes place through two very small holes in the double-headed
plug, the high pressure pre-
vailing being sufficient to
force the oil through these.
The oil enters the hole B,
shown at the top of the block,
passes round the channel C,
and out by the smaller hole
A at the bottom. When the
regulator is wide open and
the engine under full load
the difference between boiler
and steam-chest pressure will

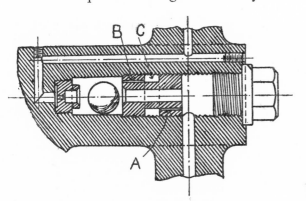

FIG. 17.—DETAIL OF BACK PRESSURE VALVE.

be only about 5 lbs. per sq. in.—not sufficient to keep the ball valve
on its seat in the double-headed plug; consequently it falls away and

the oil then feeds through the large hole in the centre of the plug, in its normal manner.

To show how this system of sight-feed lubricating has been developed, the following illustrations commencing with Fig. 18 show the complete arrangement for lubricating as adopted on one of the British railways. This is practically automatic in that the lubrication is controlled by the movement of the regulator handle. This handle points downwards,

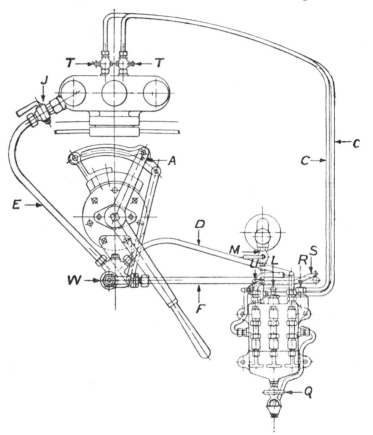

FIG. 18.—AUTOMATIC LUBRICATION ARRANGEMENT, GREAT WESTERN RAILWAY.

and has a projecting tail A which points upwards and moves over a quadrant. Above the quadrant the tail terminates in a bolt which moves in a slotted link in such a manner that the regulator handle moves about $\frac{3}{4}$ in. from the stop before the lubricator controlling valve W is opened. This valve is fixed on the fire-box front immediately below the regulator stuffing-box. The slotted link previously mentioned is fixed to a fulcrum on the left-hand side above the quadrant. At the other end the link is connected to the valve by a rod, so that when the regulator is opened beyond the initial $\frac{3}{4}$ in., the link and rod are lifted and the valve opened.   The valve controls an auxiliary steam-pipe F, and also takes oil from the sight-feed lubricator, which is fixed on the right-hand side of the fire-box front.

The regulator jockey-valve is arranged so that no steam is admitted to the steam-chest until the pointer A has moved $\frac{3}{4}$ in. from the stop, but the position of the handle between this point and the stop can be such that a little steam and oil are fed through the small $\frac{1}{2}$-in. auxiliary pipe when the engine is coasting.   In this manner the piston and valves are working in a lubricated vapour when the engine is running down a bank with the main steam to the cylinders shut off.   It had been found that with ordinary sight-feed lubrication, drops of oil delivered direct to the tops of the cylinders and the tops of the steam-chests, the oil was not distributed over the surface so evenly and so well as it was when it was distributed by the aid of the auxiliary steam-pipe.

The whole of the steam for the auxiliary steam-pipe and the lubricator is taken from a special fitting T fixed at the top of the fire-box inside the cab, and all the steam outlets are controlled by cocks.   In addition to the steam to the controlling valve and the auxiliary steam-pipe, there are two steam-pipes CC taken round the top of the cab to the lubricator. The length of these is such that the steam for the lubricator can condense in them, and the water of condensation serves to displace the oil. An additional small steam-pipe is connected to the lubricator by means of the cock M to warm the oil when required; this should only be used when the oil is too thick to feed.

The steam-atomized oil is taken from the footplate to a distribution box in the smoke-box, and from this $\frac{3}{4}$-in. oil-pipes convey the oil to the steam-pipes, into which they enter on the side between the regulator and the cylinders, or in the case of superheater engines, between the superheater and the cylinders.   The smoke-box connections, as viewed from the front, are shown in Figs. 19 to 21, of which Fig. 19 shows the arrangement for a two-cylinder engine without superheater, Fig. 20 for a similar engine with superheater, and Fig. 21 for a four-cylinder engine with superheater.   In all three illustrations O is the distribution box and F is the auxiliary steam-pipe from valve W.   In the case of each taken in conjunction with Fig. 18, the oil is fed from the sight-feeds through the oil-pipe D to the valve W.   Steam through the pipe E picks up the oil from W and carries it through the pipe F to the oil distributor O in the smoke-box, and from O the distributing pipes convey it to the steam-pipes.

Oil is fed to the regulator by displacement direct from the lubricator in the usual way through the pipe S.

The whole arrangement is such that the first steam to reach the cylinders on starting the engine comes through the $\frac{1}{2}$-in. auxiliary steam-pipe and brings a supply of oil with it. Further, when "coasting," a little steam and oil must be fed to the cylinders without moving the regulator handle far enough to open the "jockey." When the regulator handle is fully closed on its stop, the lubricator will feed a few drops and then stop altogether, and this small quantity of oil will remain in the pipes ready to be distributed to the cylinders when the engine is again started. The lubricator feed will not increase and clog the glasses when the regulator is closed, since the valve W closes with it and cuts steam off from the auxiliary steam-pipe.

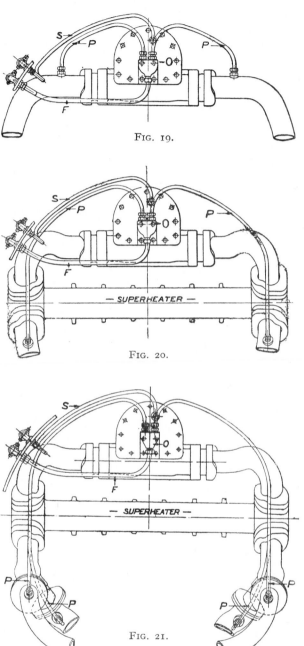

FIG. 19.

FIG. 20.

FIG. 21.

FIGS. 19–21.—CONNECTIONS OF OIL-PIPES TO STEAM-PIPES IN SMOKE-BOX, GREAT WESTERN RAILWAY.

Triple Sight-feed Lubricator.

A triple sight-feed lubricator, which has a capacity of 8 pints, is shown in detail in Fig. 22. The steam for warming the lubricator passes through the passage through the centre of the strengthening ribs A, which act as radiators for the heat. The lubricator is of the simple displacement type. The oil rises and enters the bent pipes C through the small rectangular slots B, of which there are four, each

$\frac{3}{4}$ in. long by 1/16 in. broad, in each pipe. From C the oil flows through the sight-feeds E. The left hand of the three feeds delivers oil through pipe S (Figs. 18 to 21) for the regulator, and the right-hand feed delivers oil for the cylinders to the pipe D (Fig. 18), and thence to the valve W.

The middle feed is marked as "spare," and may be used in emergency when the other glasses break or clog. When the handle L (Fig. 18), which controls the middle feed is in the "straight out" position, this feed does not work, but it may be "switched on" to cylinders or regulator by moving L through 45° into positions marked on the lubricator. The regulating spindle of the broken or clogged glass must first be shut. Should the valve W stick, the stopcock J must be closed when the engine is standing. The oil feed should not vary for different openings of the regulator.

The glasses should be examined about once a fortnight, as they are liable to corrode about the packing. They are filled with water by re-

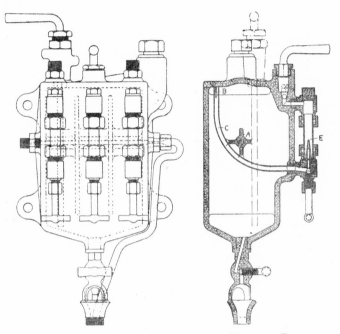

FIG. 22.—SIGHT-FEED LUBRICATOR, GREAT WESTERN RAILWAY.

moving the top plug. In the case of a burst connecting pipe CC the corresponding cock T is closed, and the handle of the cock U is moved to the position marked on the lubricator to bring the other pipe into action.

In frosty weather all water should be run out of the lubricator and condensing pipes by cock Q, before putting the engine away.

The regulator sight-feed should not be adjusted until the regulator is at least half open or it will feed too fast when the regulator is fully opened.

After filling the lubricator, the warming cock M must never be opened until the cocks U, T, T and J have been opened, or the lubricator may be burst by the expansion of the oil.

In fixing a sight-feed lubricator in the cab care should be taken that there are no " traps " or " pockets " in the oil-pipes leading to the steam-chest. Such pockets have to be filled with oil, and the time taken to fill them depends partly upon the rate of feed, and also upon the size of oil-pipe and the shape and length of the " pocket." Moreover, oil-pipes which are run horizontally for part of their length form a " trap " when the engine is running up a steep incline, since there is then a fall in such length towards the lubricator instead of towards the cylinders. The pipes are best arranged to have, if possible, a steady fall from lubricator to steam-chest steeper than the rise of the heaviest gradient on the line.

In some engines the oil is delivered above vertical slide-valves through a pipe perforated with small holes in that portion immediately above the valves, and the oil falls through these holes in the form of spray.

Before filling the lubricator with oil the steam-valves and drain cock should be properly closed, and attention should be paid to all valve seats to see that they do not leak. Before refilling the oil reservoir the drain cock at the bottom of the lubricator is opened to let out the water of condensation. Steam should be admitted gradually to allow the sight-feed glasses to fill slowly, since if steam be turned on too quickly a violent disturbance of the oil will occur and the glasses will cloud up.

Finally, the oil supply should be regulated by means of the oil-regulating valves. The quantity of oil to be delivered will vary with the engine and the work it is doing from about six to twelve drops per minute. The lubricator when working properly should " cut off " the oil-drops squarely and at equal intervals of time. The oil feeds should be started some ten or fifteen minutes before the engine begins work.

Clouding of the glass is sometimes due to the driver opening the oil-regulating valve too soon and too far before the sight-feed glass has filled up with condensed water. In this case the oil travels up the side of the glass, to which the particles stick. To prevent this designs have been produced in which a wire is fitted in the delivery nipple of the sight-feed glass, up which the drops of oil will mount instead of clinging to the side of the glass.

The lubricator should not be allowed to work so long that the oil is completely displaced; refilling should be done before this happens, otherwise the lubricator becomes too hot. Not only is there danger of breaking the sight-feed glasses, but when the lubricator is restarted the steam does not condense until the reservoir has cooled. This applies more particularly to lubricators of the older types without separate condenser and with steam admitted at the top. These older patterns are not always provided with expansion chambers or excess pressure relief valves, and in such cases the lubricator should not be completely filled with oil, but a little space left for the expansion of the oil when heated, and also for admitting the condensed steam.

An important point in regard to the regulation of the flow of oil lies in the " choke " or small nipple usually placed at the outer end of the delivery pipe. After the engine has been in service for some time it may be found that the oil is running away too fast through one or more of the sight-feeds. The " chokes " or nipples should then be examined, and if found to be worn and enlarged they should be replaced, or the " chokes " reversed if of the pattern shown in Fig. 23.

The lubricator should be cleaned at regular intervals of about two and a half to three months. The reservoir is emptied and filled up with paraffin oil, after which it should be allowed to stand to dissolve out any gummy deposits. The paraffin having been run out, the filling inlet is then closed and steam blown through the lubricator to remove the dissolved deposits through the drain cock. The connecting oil-pipes may be cleaned by running thin petroleum through them; this acts as a solvent of the thick oil which is liable to clog them up.

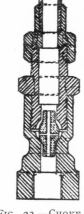

FIG. 23.—CHOKE FOR " DETROIT " LUBRICATOR.

In very cold weather the lubricant should be emptied before putting the engine away to obviate any liability of the contents freezing and bursting the oil container.

When running with steam on the steam-chest requires more oil than the cylinders, but with steam off the cylinders require more than the steam-chest. This applies to engines with the valves between or below the cylinders, as these drop away from the port faces when steam is shut off. When the valves are on the top the oil feed to them should not be reduced when steam is shut off.

With sight-feed lubricators the oil is delivered on a time basis independently of the speed of the engine. When the engine is working heavily and slowly up a bank more oil is required, and the number of drops of oil delivered per mile is increased. At high speeds with steam on the quantity delivered is less per mile, and as less is required under these working conditions, the sight-feed lubricator adapts itself, so to speak, automatically to the work to be done. When steam is off, the variation in feed should be very slight, since in the best lubricators of the " hydrostatic " type the feed depends upon the height of the column of water, as previously explained. If, however, the lubricator is of an old pattern and has been so constructed that the pressures of steam at the inlet and delivery are not equalized, then it will feed an excess of oil when the engine is " coasting," because there is no pressure in the steam-chest or cylinders. The uniform feed and back pressure valve (Fig. 17) of the Wakefield sight-feed lubricator already referred to is for the purpose of overcoming the defect.

Mechanical Lubricators.

Earlier mechanical lubricators contained only one piston plunger, and the various oil deliveries branched off from what might be termed a central oil main. As the oil tends to flow more freely down the nearest branches, to the detriment of those farther away, such a system had grave disadvantages, and has been abandoned. It is now the universal practice to have a lubricator containing a separate pump for each delivery, which, being independent, can be regulated to suit the quantity of oil required for the part which it supplies.

A good mechanical lubricator should be simple and with as few moving parts liable to get out of order as possible. Owing to the high speed of the locomotive, the internal friction of the lubricator should be reduced to the lowest possible limit. The pins and levers should be large enough and have sufficient bearing area to stand the constant wear. This is a point that is occasionally overlooked in some designs. An important point is that each pump should have a high volumetric efficiency, since the viscosity of the oil varies with a change of temperature, and considerable differences in the quantity of oil delivered would result.

There should be simple and accessible means of quickly regulating the quantity of oil delivered by each separate feed. The oil reservoir should be fitted with a wire-gauze strainer and an oil-warming pipe; and a very useful addition, not met with on all lubricators, is a gauge glass or level to show the quantity of oil remaining in the reservoir.

In some foreign patterns there are six deliveries with plungers of various diameters, so that each part to be lubricated receives its proper proportion of oil. This, however, is an unnecessary refinement, provided that with equal plungers to all deliveries, each one can be regulated independently, as is done in British practice.

Briefly stated, the following are the principal advantages of mechanical lubricators:

1. They supply oil from the moment the engine starts to move, and deliver oil when steam is shut off and the engine is " coasting."

2. They stop feeding when the engine stops, so that no oil is wasted whilst it is standing.

3. They are independent of the steam supply.

The number of feeds for cylinder and valve lubrication is usually six or eight. In the case of six-feed lubrication the cylinders have two delivery pipes and the valves four. Eight-feed lubricators have two additional connections to the piston tail rod bushes.

The usual practice in this country is to fix the lubricator on the platform between the driving splashers and the smoke-box. Most engineers prefer to keep the lubricator out of the cab, where not only would it occupy space, but might also distract the attention of the driver. On the other hand, drives have been arranged to suit the fixing of mechanical lubricators inside the cab, where, should anything go wrong, the defect is noticed immediately.

Arrangements are made for warming the oil during cold weather, and it is of great importance that the driver should not neglect to open the warming valve during such periods. Cases have occurred in which, owing to neglect of this precaution, the oil has become so thick that the mechanical lubricator would not work properly, with the result that the valves have seized and caused damage to the motion of the engine.

A section of Wakefield's No. 1 double-acting mechanical lubricator is shown in Fig. 24. The design of the pumps is such that differential plungers force the oil forward on both strokes of the pump. This does not deliver double the quantity of oil, but the same quantity is spread equally over both strokes. A reciprocating motion is given to the crosshead by means of the eccentric shaft L. The large and small pump barrels are cross-connected; the right-hand large pump delivers into the chamber of the corresponding left-hand small pump, and vice versa. Taking the case of the right-hand pump, when the crosshead moves from right to left, oil is drawn past the right-hand suction valve C into the large pump barrel E, and on the return stroke the valve C closes and the oil is forced past the intermediate valve D into the small barrel H on the left-hand side of the lubricator, the plungers J of which are hollow. As the small pump barrel contains only one-half of the quantity of oil contained in the large barrel, the surplus, after the small barrel is filled, is forced into the steam-chest and cylinders through the delivery. The oil remaining in the small barrel is forced away on the opposite stroke, i.e. when the large plunger is on the suction stroke; this ensures a steady flow of oil. The oil-feed is regulated from the outside of the lubricator. Each of the pump barrels is furnished with an adjustable plug G, and the feed to any one of the outlets can be varied by merely altering the position of this regulating plug. When the latter is screwed right home, the pump is working at full capacity. The stroke of the pump is $\frac{3}{8}$ in., and one full turn outwards of G decreases the pump stroke by 1/16 in.—*i.e.* the amount of oil delivered is reduced by one-sixth. At B there is a wire-gauze strainer, and the oil-warming pipe passes through at K.

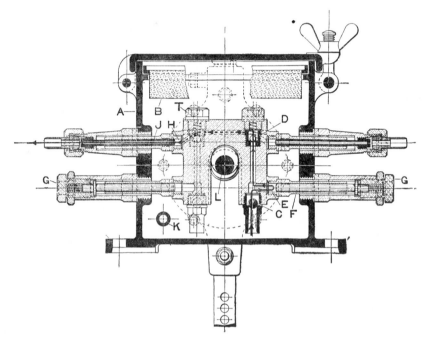

Fig. 24.—Wakefield No. 1 Mechanical Lubricator.

It is advisable to fit back pressure or check-valves close to the points to be lubricated. These valves are loaded to a predetermined pressure by means of a spring in such a way that the lubricator pump when working can overcome it and force the oil through them to the steam-chest and cylinders; but when steam is shut off, the steam-chest vacuum is insufficient to open the valve and empty the oil-pipes between it and the lubricator. The valves should be placed as close as possible to the inlets into the steam-chest and cylinders. The oil delivery pipe is therefore fully charged throughout its length and continues to deliver the oil at a regular rate instead of having the oil sucked out of it in " gulps."

Grease Lubrication.

The successful development of the use of grease as a lubricant for locomotives is perhaps due to American practice more than any other. For some years past great attempts have been made to obtain longer runs with reduced attention for engines, and grease as a lubricant has had an important influence on this.

There is considerable difference in the conditions imposed in the use of grease as compared with oil. Any sign of heating of a bearing when the latter is in use causes some anxiety to those responsible, whilst with grease heating may show nothing but the proper functioning of the material used. To a driver, therefore, it will take some little time to get accustomed to these changed conditions, as it may be that with a bearing lubricated with oil he may feel he must use great care with it, whilst with grease the same indication may be only a safe heat which ensures satisfactory working.

With grease-fed axle-boxes a block, or pad, of grease is placed in the "keep" and held up to the journal by coiled springs under a perforated steel plate; this latter being shaped to suit the radius of the journal. When a predetermined temperature is reached, grease will be automatically fed up through the holes in the curved plate to the journal. A block of grease will wear away to the extent of about an inch in running from 5000 to 6000 miles on express trains, but if properly fitted with suitable bearings, no attention will be required other than replacement of grease at intervals. With coupling and connecting rods, gudgeon pins and valve-return crank, etc., a special nipple, or plug, is substituted for the usual cap—that is, screwed into the oil receptacle, and the outer end of this is designed to be connected up with a high-pressure "gun," or pump. The practice is to confine a volume of grease in an air-tight receptacle, making provision for forcing it by pressure into the bearing before the start of every run; then, as a bearing becomes warm, the grease will feed down gradually and automatically.

In India, South Africa and the Colonies, grease lubrication is rapidly replacing oil, and is being extended to the valve-gear, brake and spring rigging, horn-block slides, bogie centres, etc., and there is much in favour of it. A soft grease, similar to petroleum jelly, is used for these parts, and is applied in the same manner as with coupling and connecting rods—that is to say, with nipples and a force pump or "gun." Apart from obtaining longer runs without attention, there is a great advantage in that the grease is applied by the running-shed staff, so that little claim is made upon the driver in preparing his engine; all his efforts can be centred upon operation. Furthermore, there is considerable economy, as the feed of grease only takes place when the engine is actually running, whereas with oil it occurs whether running or stationary; unless, of course, the men concerned are very careful and have the opportunity to remove the trimmings from the syphon, tubes, etc.

The " Isothermos " Axle-box.

A form of lubrication for tender axle-boxes which has latterly attained favour is a mechanical one. A disc attached to the end of the journal and dipping into an oil reservoir acts as a feeder of lubricant to the journal. Fig. 25 illustrates one of the most recent forms applicable to axle-boxes of locomotive tenders, Diesel, electric, and other engines.

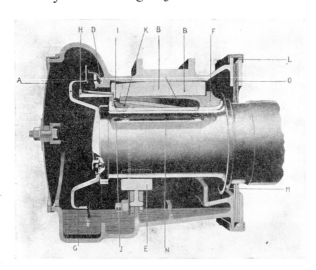

In principle the axle-box is simple in the extreme; a " dipper " or " palette " secured to the end of the journal revolving in an oil-bath at the front of the axle-box picks up and distributes a constant supply of oil to the journal. Referring to the illustration, Fig. 25, the palette G rotating with the journal (to which it is

FIG. 25.—SECTION OF " ISOTHERMOS " AXLE-BOX.

firmly attached) picks up oil, and carries and delivers it to the upper part of the axle-box, by centrifugal force and by drip. That thrown up by the former, collects and runs into the channel D, from which it is conveyed to one or more openings in the tray H of the block B to the bearing. Oil not delivered by centrifugal force drips from the extremities of the palette G into the tray H. The oil is distributed along the journal through the passages I, J and K.

Oil dripping from both sides of the bush F along its full length falls into two outer filtering trays E, where any grit will settle in the partitions as it passes along on its return to the reservoir.

The obturating ring M is an important detail ensuring, as it does, the prevention of oil passing out by the dust-shield. The drip from this is collected on the sloping surface, and passes a central filter tray E before finding its way back to the reservoir.

A filling plug can be provided at the sides of the axle-box for the introduction of oil, and for checking the level in the reservoir when desired.

When needed, a plug of metal, fusible at a low temperature, can be arranged in the axle-box front in such a manner that, should heating develop (a very unexpected event), the plug will melt and allow smoke to escape, and thus indicate the existence of possible trouble.

In practice, with this axle-box, rolling-stock fitted with it is not returned to depots for attention to lubrication, and bearings are only inspected when the vehicles are called in for periodical general overhaul. Once filled and put into service, Isothermos axle-boxes function for long periods without attention; it is very desirable, therefore, that only oil of best quality should be used.

In confirmation of the statement that this system not only lubricates but cools the bearings, it should be noted that at 25 m.p.h. the revolving palette delivers the equivalent of from 3 to 4 gallons of oil per hour to the journal.

To meet arguments such as reliability after long standing-off periods of filled vehicles, any detrimental action of the palette on the oil used, unsuitability for tropical or extreme cold climates, etc., perhaps the best reply is a reference to the long list of using railways all over the world, in all climates and under widely different conditions.

For vehicles which are subject to tipping, a special type of isothermos axle-box is available, which can be completely reversed without loss of oil.

To meet the special requirements of countries such as India, where the railways suffer heavy loss from theft, and where unskilled native labour is employed, a simplified form of box which is proof against theft of oil or any interference has been prepared.

Peyinghaus Axle-box.

Constructed on principles which comply with the accepted deductions on lubricated bearings originally dictated by the experiments of Mr. Beauchamp Tower, as far back as 1883, the arrangement now described secures retention of fluid friction, between the bearing surfaces, as opposed to the surface friction experienced with ordinary solid bearings, and rolling friction attributed to roller and ball-bearings.

The term " lower feed lubrication " applied to bearings subjected to upward load pressure refers to any method of lubrication wherein the lubricating oil is conveyed outside the loaded surface of the bearing to the revolving journal, and carried by the latter to the bearing surfaces, whereas with " upper feed lubrication " the lubricant is delivered to the journal between it and the loaded surface of the bearing.

The " upper feed lubrication " system, as illustrated in Fig. 26, is more or less condemned by the results recorded in the experiments mentioned, because in consequence of the rise in pressure of the film of oil due to the wedging action taking place in every sliding friction bearing, the central oil inlet not only fails to

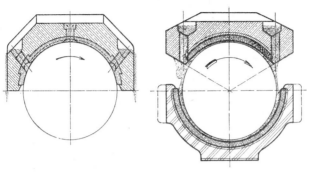

FIG. 26.   FIG. 27.

permit the entry of any oil from above but, on the contrary, owing to the excessive pressure prevailing at this point, allows oil to be forced out of and away from the bearing. This defect is clearly shown in the drawing, wherein the back flow of lubricant through the upper hole is represented by small arrows.

The means taken to rectify these conditions and secure the correct application of the lubricating oil will become evident when comparison is made with Fig. 27, which illustrates the ideal solution, i.e. lower feed lubrication as embodied

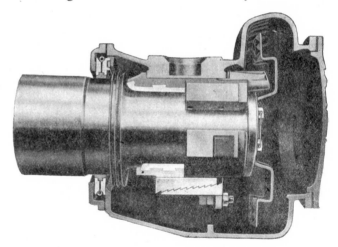

FIG. 28.—PEYINGHAUS AXLE-BOX.

in the axle-box bearing we now direct attention to.

Fig. 28 represents in section the Peyinghaus axle-box bearing with portions of the brasses cut away. This shows a capacious casing, or body, designed not only to accommodate the rotating oil distributor, but to form a receptacle for a considerable quantity of oil. At the same time, owing to its large, exposed surface, it provides a very efficient means for rapidly cooling off any oil heated during its passage through the loaded bearing zone.

CHAPTER VII

Tenders—Tanks—Water Filling—Oil-tanks—Bunkers—Brake Gear—Condensing—
Water Pick-up, etc.

THE tender is an important and necessary adjunct to a locomotive intended for use on long runs. Its capacity in this country will range from 2500 to 5000 gallons of water, and carry from four to eight tons of coal, according to the size and power of the engine it accompanies and the service intended to work on.

General Arrangement.

A typical example of a six-wheeled tender as used on a British railway is shown in Fig. 1. The wheels are spaced about equal distances apart, and have axle-boxes with springs above, outside the framing, and as accessible as possible. Roller bearings are now being used for large tenders, to reduce the power required for the haulage of such heavy vehicles.

The outer frames carrying the axle-box guides are generally about $\frac{7}{8}$ in. thick, and these are stayed to inner frames of moderate depth ($\frac{3}{4}$ in. thick), running the full length of the tender framing. This construction permits of a "well," or lower tank, being provided for securing a good water capacity, also offering ready means for attaching brake gear, stays, etc.

Water Tanks.

Electric welding is becoming common now for the joints of tank plates—$\frac{1}{4}$ in. to 5/16 in. thick—and fastening the angle iron stiffeners to tanks, bunkers, etc. This enables dead-weight to be reduced, and gives additional capacity by omission of so many angles, butt-strips, rivet-heads, etc. In the water tanks, suitable wash-plates are introduced to prevent the water washing about from end to end when the brakes are applied and a quick stoppage made. The coal bunker is said to be of "self-trimming" type when the bottom and sides are built with inclined plates so that the coal falls towards the front centre, Fig. 2.

149

FIG. 1.—4000-GALLON TENDER FOR "CASTLE" CLASS LOCOMOTIVES, G.W.R.

FIG. 2.—ARRANGEMENT OF COAL SPACE ON TENDER, G.W.R.

Filling-hole.

The water filling-hole is mostly placed to the rear, although in some instances it is arranged in front. When fitted with water " pick-up " apparatus (as most tenders for main line service now are), the delivery from the pick-up is adjacent to the filling-hole. The raising and lowering of the pick-up is performed by either hand or power (compressed air

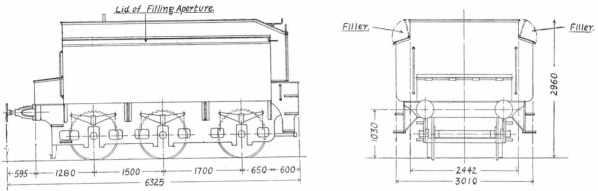

FIG. 3.—LOCOMOTIVE TENDER, AUSTRIAN STATE RAILWAYS.

or vacuum), the power from the brake equipment being used in the latter case. Fig. 3 illustrates a tender wherein the filling aperture extends the full length of the tank; this allows latitude in the distance travelled when stopping to take water.

Coupling between Engine and Tender.

The coupling between the engine and tender is of various designs, all intended to provide a safe and flexible, as well as steady, fastening, more or less permanent, as it is seldom needed to separate an engine from its tender except when taken to shops. The usual arrangement consists of a substantial draw-bar, with spring attached, and short side buffers with safety links, as precautions against any rupture of the main draw-bar.

Details of a very solid device are shown in Fig. 4.

In this arrangement all buffers, springs, etc., are avoided; it consists of a steel casting carried on a plate extension of the tender framing. Into this latter is fixed, by means of suitable bushes, a steel ball having a vertical passage through it, into which the connecting pin is dropped. On the engine the pin is retained by members formed in the drag-box above and below the ball housing, and can be withdrawn by means of a grip-ring through a small flap in the cab floor, should necessity arise for separating the engine from the tender. Wear in the ball bushing is provided against by making the rear half of the bush adjustable by a screw-locked vertical wedge, and a play of 105 mm. (4·13 in.), up and down.

As the shifting of the centre of articulation to a solitary point

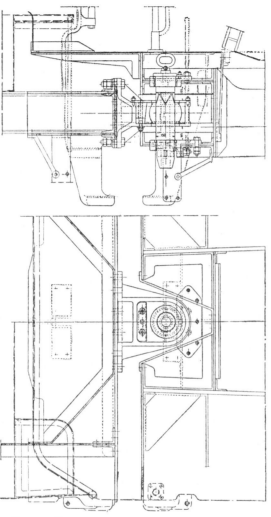

FIG. 4.—DETAILS OF TENDER COUPLING, ITALIAN STATE RAILWAYS.

beneath the engine some distance forward of that formerly taken involves an increase in the angularity of relative displacement when traversing curves, it has been found desirable to allow a greater side play to the forward bogie of the tender, and this now amounts to 2·36 in. each way.

In addition to the essential simplicity of the new coupling, it has the further advantage of making it possible to use a single footplate extending from the engine almost to the coal-shute on the tender, thus giving a much steadier foothold to the fireman and rendering his work less laborious.

A more refined fitment which has become popular in recent days is illustrated in Fig. 5. A strong adjustable bar is provided, which has ball joints at each end, permitting of freedom of movement laterally, whilst assuring a definite and reliable connection in tension or compression.

Buffers.

For attachment to vehicles forming a train, standard buffers and couplings are fitted at the rear of the tender.

As buffers are of some importance in connection with the running and stability of a locomotive, a diagram of spring curves is given in Fig. 6, which shows graphically the following characteristics of three typical standards in construction:

(A) Standard for India, b.g.   Nip ¾-in. travel before contact with inner spring, 2 in.

(B) British type (1).   Nip 1⅛-in. travel before contact with inner spring, 3 in.

(C) British type (2).   Nip 1⅛-in. travel before contact with inner spring, 2½ in.

All the above mentioned are fitted with compound springs—that is, one within the other, the second being arranged to come into action after so many inches of travel of the outer spring.   An initial " nip " is always given to a buffer spring to keep the parts in good contact, which in these cases is, of course, on the outer spring only, the inner one being entirely free.

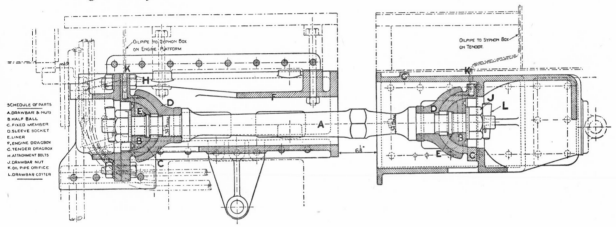

FIG. 5.—GOODALL'S ENGINE AND TENDER COUPLING.

In these compound spring buffers normal shocks are easily absorbed by the range permitted to the outer spring, whilst more severe shocks come on both springs, which can be made to have an ultimate capacity of from 50 to 100 per cent. above that of the single outer spring.   In buffers of the plunger type the inner spring is retained in position by a ring of special profile which is held solidly by the nip in the outer spring; by this means the inner spring is kept correctly in position.

Feed Delivery.

The feed-water from the tank is passed through strainers before entering the feed-pipes leading to the engine injectors or pumps. Suitable cocks are provided, whereby the flow of water can be controlled from the tender.   Fig. 7 illustrates an approved connection composed of metal pipes and fittings obviating the use of rubber.

Many large tenders now run on bogies, as the weight, in running order, with coal and water, may be excessive for only three axles; with

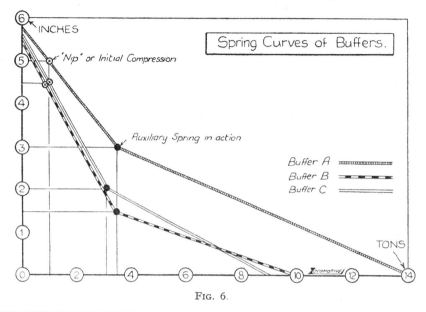

Fig. 6.

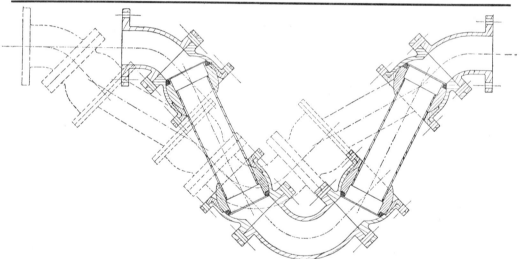

Fig. 7.—" Flexstel " Expansion Joint for Feed between Engine and Tender. Dotted lines show range of movement.

four axles the load is distributed more in accordance with permanent way restrictions.

Brake Gear.

At the front of the tender, or footplate end, the tool-boxes, water-gauge and hand-brake are provided. The latter usually operates the brake-blocks on all the wheels, the power being equally distributed through equalizing beams and levers designed to apply pressure (up to 80 per cent. or 90 per cent. of the partly empty tender) with an ordinary application, the heavy vehicle then acting as an important retarding agent. The brake gear is also generally equipped with power cylinders (steam, air or vacuum), arranged to operate in conjunction with the continuous brakes on the train. Fig. 8 gives in diagram form the arrangement of levers L for a six-wheeled tender, from which the power P can be easily calculated.

Brake-blocks.

These are of cast-iron, and being of softer metal than the steel of the tyres, they suffer most wear from the brakes, and are easily replaced

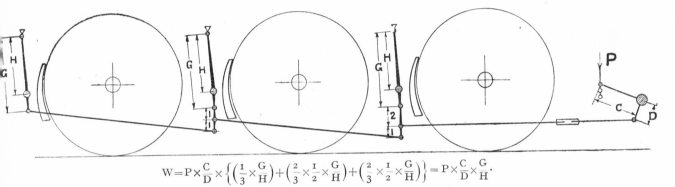

$$W = P \times \frac{C}{D} \times \left\{ \left(\frac{1}{3} \times \frac{G}{H} \right) + \left(\frac{2}{3} \times \frac{1}{2} \times \frac{G}{H} \right) + \left(\frac{2}{3} \times \frac{1}{2} \times \frac{G}{H} \right) \right\} = P \times \frac{C}{D} \times \frac{G}{H}.$$

FIG. 8.—ENGINE OR TENDER BRAKE ARRANGEMENT WITH COMPENSATING BRAKE GEAR.

when worn out. Various compounds for the metal of brake-blocks, or shoes, have been used, but the best results appear to have been obtained with ordinary cast-iron. Brake-blocks in British brakes are so formed that they bear upon the tread of the tyre, or that portion which runs on the rails. The two wearing influences, of course, tend to augment wear of the tyre, but it is preferred to tolerate this rather than adopt the custom prevalent in America and elsewhere for providing blocks with a portion to bear upon the flanges of the tyres, inclining to reduce them and maintain the original section of tyre.

With cast-iron brake-blocks, the friction between the block and tyre depends on the speed of the train; it is low at high, and increases with lower speeds. It follows that with a constant brake pressure the braking force is less at high speeds where there is need for braking on long distances. Experience has shown that certain minerals possess more uniform friction than cast-iron at varying speed. Granite and basalt are better adapted for such purposes on account of their hardness and resistance to wear. Granite gives a rather better coefficient of friction than basalt. If the two minerals are mixed in an approved manner, intermediate strengths can be obtained; mixed with cement by the addition of water, and pressed in suitable moulds and then left to harden, will form blocks with more coefficients of friction for different speeds. With a proper mixture, coefficients of high value are obtained, so that the braking force between the wheel and rail is entirely utilized at all speeds, thus shortening the braking period. To get higher co-efficients of friction, basalt can be cast alone or mixed with granite and poured in liquid form into moulds to form the blocks. Although basalt and granite are bad conductors of electricity, the dust made when braking does not constitute so great a danger to locomotives and electric conductors as the dust produced by cast-iron now used.

At the bottom end of the brake-hangers, crossbeams, or tie-rods, are provided. These fulfil two functions: the power from the pull-rods being transmitted through them to the hangers, whilst they also draw the latter together, tending to prevent spreading when the brakes are applied.

In most cases the hanging of the brake gear is so arranged that for purposes of release, gravity is sufficient to remove the brake-blocks from the wheels; where there is insufficient, release springs are provided.

Tank Locomotives.

In the cases of tank locomotives carrying supplies of fuel and water on their framing, the tanks can be rectangular and placed on the sides of the engine, or may be of the "saddle" type, suitably shaped to occupy a position above the boiler. These latter, however, must always be of somewhat limited capacity, due to axle-load restrictions and load-gauge limits. When a tank locomotive is required to carry more water than can be conveniently accommodated in side tanks built along the under-frame, a third tank is placed below the coal bunker at the rear, all the tanks being coupled up with pipes to allow the water to equalize itself over the wheel-base of the locomotive. A tank engine equipped in this manner will carry 2000 to 2500 gallons of water, and from 2 to 3 tons of coal.

In Figs. 9 and 9A a tank locomotive of modern design and construction is shown wherein the main portion of the water supply is contained in a large rectangular tank, placed between the frames and extending from the front of the smoke-box to the fire-box. This tank also has a "well," or additional chamber, between the leading and middle coupled axles. The total capacity for water exceeds 2500 gallons, and the disposition of the tank ensures a very low centre of gravity, with a resultant very steady engine on a track which cannot be rated as first-class.

FIG. 9.—4–6–4 PASSENGER TANK LOCOMOTIVE, TURKISH RAILWAYS.

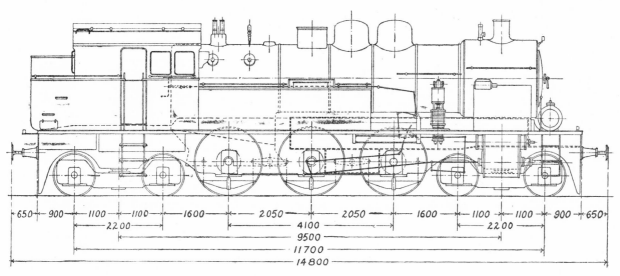

FIG. 9A.—4–6–4 PASSENGER TANK LOCOMOTIVE, TURKISH RAILWAYS.

Condensing Exhaust Steam.

Another condition has often to be met with in tank engines which are called upon to do part of their running on underground railways. It is expedient that the exhaust steam should be effectively condensed when the engine is running in tunnels, hence pipes are provided to convey part, or all, of the exhaust steam from the base of the blast-pipe in the smoke-box to the water tanks, in which it is projected on to the surface of the water. Fig. 10 gives the general arrangement of such apparatus. A is a half-end view, B elevation, and C a half-plan. Escape pipes are therefore installed to allow any surplus steam to reach the atmosphere without pressure accumulating in the tanks. The control of this condensing arrangement is effected by providing flap-valves (D) at the base of the blast-pipe, which are operated by the driver from the cab.

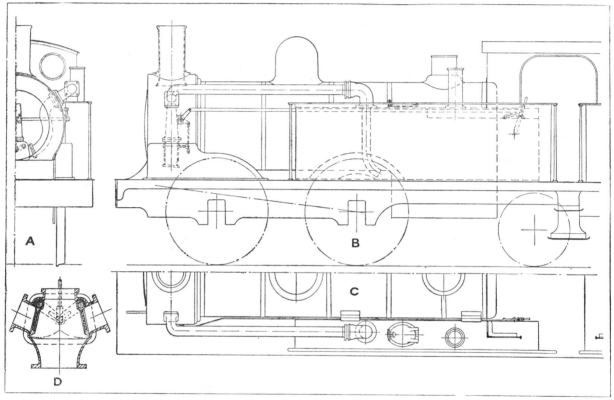

FIG. 10.—CONDENSING ARRANGEMENT FOR TANK ENGINE.

Water Pick-up.

A most important detail in the equipment of main line tenders in this country is the "pick-up" for water to replenish the tender tank whilst the engine is running. This, of course, obviates the need for carrying large quantities of water for engines on long runs. As originally adopted in the 'sixties, in its elementary form, it consisted of a hinged pipe lowered by hand into a track tank, from which the water was scooped up while the tender passed over it at high speed. Needless to say, a large percentage of water was lost by this primitive method of using a plain square-ended receiving pipe. Now, approved arrangements have deflectors provided which tend to direct the flow of water into the scoop and also prevent the bulk of the water being splashed to one side.

These latter improvements have been the means of saving nearly 20 per cent. in picking up, and 50 per cent. in loss by splashing—high figures when millions of gallons of water are used per day. Fig. 12 overleaf shows the arrangement as applied to a tank engine intended to pick up water while running in either direction. Diagram, Fig. 11,

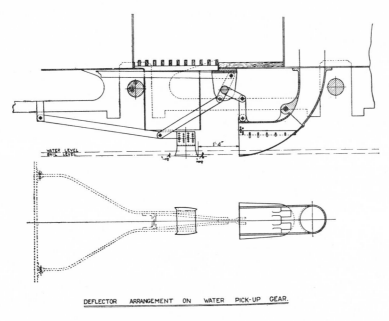

DEFLECTOR ARRANGEMENT ON WATER PICK-UP GEAR.

FIG. 11.

gives clearly the action of the deflectors. The scoop can be operated by hand—or, better, power, secured by utilizing the compressed air or vacuum of the brake service.

Tests of Pick-up Apparatus.

Some few years ago a series of tests were made on the old Midland Railway, and the present form of device was adopted from the results of these experiments. In the drawing will be noticed the lower portion of a chamber built into the tender. This accommodated an observer who travelled in the tender to note what happened as it passed over the water-troughs. A considerable number of passenger express engine tests were made over the troughs at various predetermined speeds. The engine was started from the same spot for each test, about two

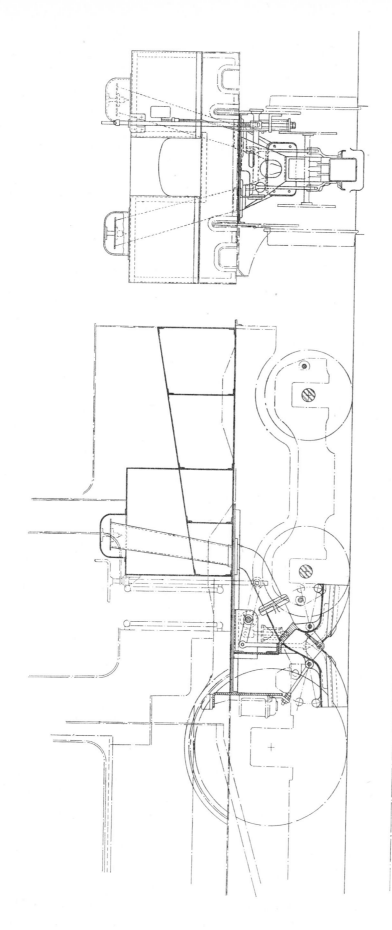
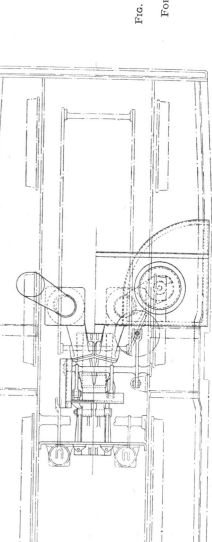

Fig. 12.—Water Pick-up arrangement as applied to Tank Engines. For operation in either direction.

miles from the troughs, and the correct speed over the troughs checked by an observer on the footplate. At the commencement of each test, and immediately afterwards, the position of the scoop fully lowered was checked over and the quantity of water picked up noted. Each run was commenced with 700 gallons of water in the tank, and the boiler of the engine full, so that there was no necessity to operate the injector between the actual start and the finish of taking the water. The scoop was fully lowered the whole length of the trough, and the water in this carefully regulated to a height of 5 inches. The water pick-up was adjusted in each case for an initial dip of the scoop of 2 inches.

The outcome of the experiments was, as stated above, the adoption of the deflector arrangement, which clearly demonstrated the following advantages:

1. The average increase of water pick-up on all speeds of about 200 gallons, representing about 17 per cent. improvement on the ordinary plain pick-up.

2. The amount of water picked up remains constant for all speeds between the minimum, or critical speed, and 60 miles per hour. It was noted that as the speed increased the amount of water splash, causing waste, also increased.

3. The reduction of water lost by splash is constant for all speeds, and was about 400 gallons, representing a reduction of about 50 per cent. at a speed of 40 miles per hour. The water splash, as a percentage of the total water taken from the trough, is as follows:

	Speed 20 m.p.h.	Speed 60 m.p.h.
Maximum Speed—Without Deflector	20 %	50 %
With Deflector .	8 %	30 %

Steam Booster Tenders.

From the very early days of steam locomotives there have been proposals to utilize the tender as an auxiliary power unit, and several tenders were equipped with cylinders and driving gear in this country to enhance the hauling power of locomotives engaged in mineral traffic. Steam was taken from the engine's boiler through a flexible connecting pipe, and the exhaust was delivered into the tender tank to act as a feed-heater. The results were only satisfactory to a degree; the chief objection was the inability of the boiler to make sufficient steam to feed a double engine; the wear and tear of the additional driving gear when not really required for power, and the difficulty of dealing with trains of the length these locomotives with their steam tenders could handle when working to full capacity.

The idea of utilizing the tender, however, has received a new impetus in recent years, owing to the successful adoption of " booster " engines to the tender. A great number of these arrangements are now in service in America, and Fig. 13 shows the adaptation to an ordinary six-wheeled

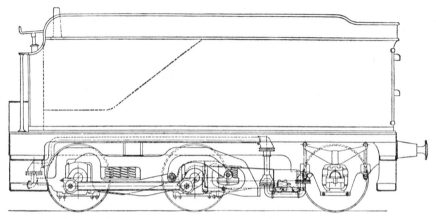

FIG. 13.—ARRANGEMENT OF BOOSTER FOR SIX-WHEELED TENDER.

tender as used in this country, the four leading wheels are fitted to a bogie frame and connected up by coupling rods to provide an auxiliary engine of considerable adhesive capacity, of much assistance in starting heavy loads and when negotiating exceptional grades. An ingenious development has been incorporated in an articulated engine and tender on the L. & N.E. Railway, illustrated in Figs. 14 and 14a.

The rear end of the engine and the front end of the tender are carried on a common steam-driven bogie, which tends to limit any lateral movement between them, and ensures a very steady running machine, possessing very considerable capacity to overcome resistance when starting, and handle increased loads on gradients.

In this case, as well as those where the " booster " engine has been installed, gear is provided by which the engine and all its motion is " cut out " of action when not required, thereby removing one of the objections of the original steam tenders. It can be " cut in " at speeds up to 30 m.p.h.

The tractive power of the engine illustrated is 22,000 lbs., which can be increased to 27,000 lbs. by putting the booster into action. As evidence of how the starting effort can be augmented on this engine, it is stated that with a train of 300 tons behind the tender, on a gradient of 1 in 70, a speed of 25 m.p.h. was reached in 5¾ minutes, with the booster bogie in operation, whereas without it only 18 m.p.h. was reached in 8 minutes. In starting, a train of 746 tons on a level road with the booster, a draw-bar pull of 12¼ tons was recorded, whereas

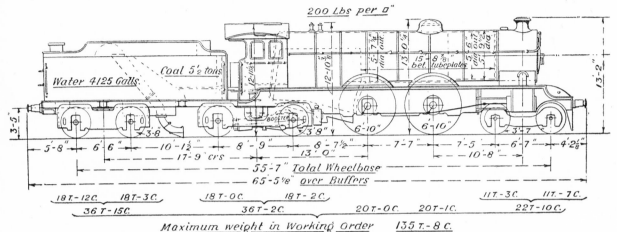

FIG. 14.—4-4-2 TYPE LOCOMOTIVE, AS CONVERTED AND FITTED WITH BOOSTER AND ARTICULATED TENDER, L. & N.E. RAILWAY.

without the assistance of the auxiliary only 496 tons could be handled with a pull of 9.8 tons developed.

A diagram of the steam booster's piping valve arrangement and gear is given, Fig. 15, with a descriptive note, as follows: When the boiler steam cock No. 1 is opened, it allows steam to pass through pipe (1) to the reverse lever pilot valve No. 2 and to the clutch safety piston valve No. 34. The steam unseats valve No. 35, allowing steam to pass through pipe (12) to clutch safety piston cylinder No. 36, thus preventing idler gear No. 14 accidentally rocking over and

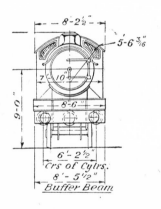

FIG. 14a.

damaging gears. The boiler steam cock No. 37, when opened, allows steam to flow through pipe (13) to preliminary throttle valve No. 6 and seating valve No. 8. Main throttle valve cock No. 43 is opened, and the booster is now ready for operation.

To operate the booster, depress reverse lever pilot valve No. 2 by raising booster latch No. 3; this unseats valve No. 4 and seats valve No. 5, and allows the steam to flow through pipe (2) to clutch safety piston control valve No. 34. This moves the piston No. 38 in the direction

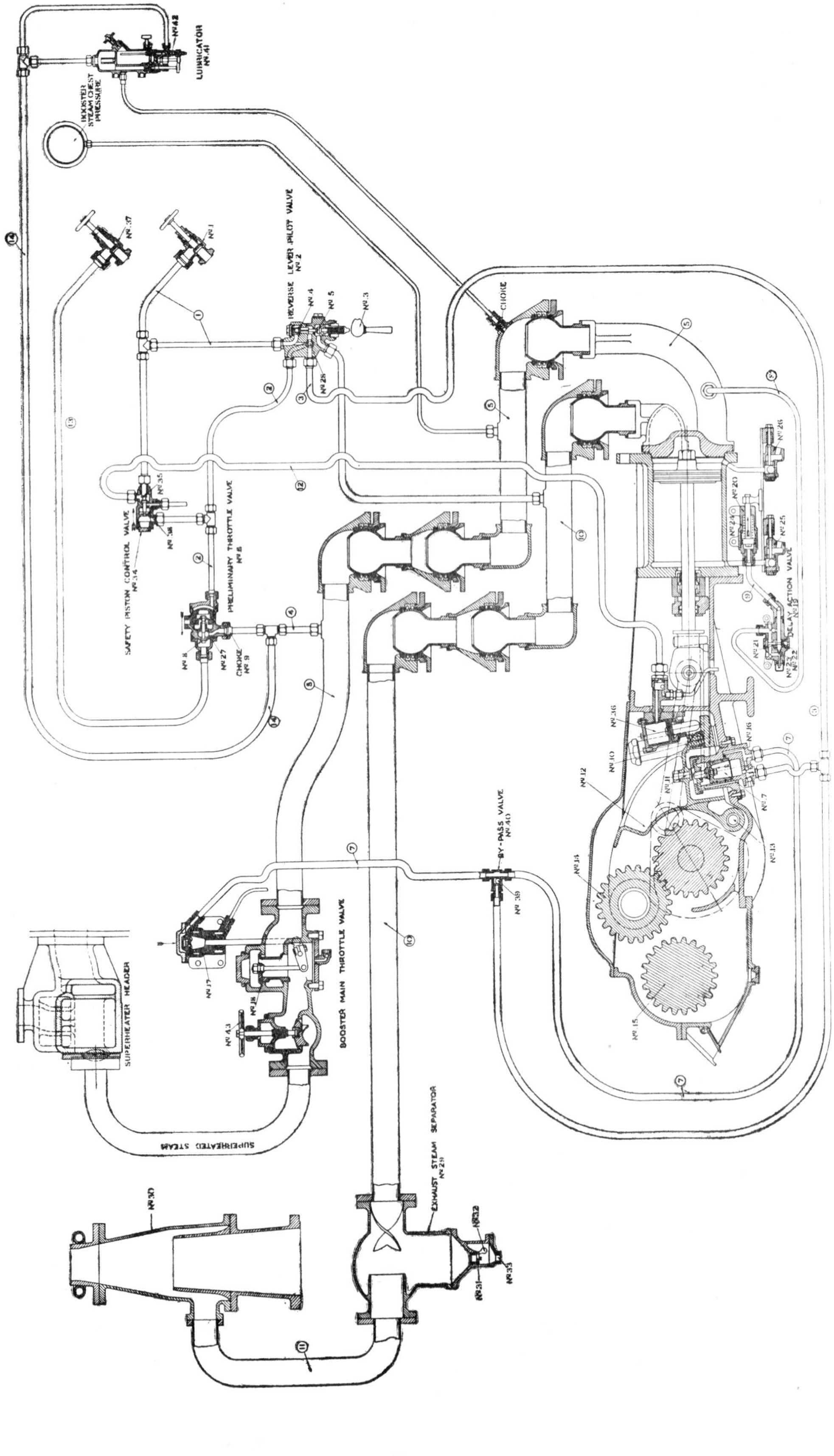

FIG. 15.—DIAGRAM OF STEAM-CONTROLLED BOOSTER FOR L. & N.E. RAILWAY PASSENGER LOCOMOTIVE.

of arrow, which seats valve No. 35, thus cutting off steam to clutch safety piston No. 36, and leaving the gears free to rock about the centre No. 13. The steam in pipe (2) flows on to preliminary throttle valve No. 6 and on to clutch cylinder No. 7 through pipe (3). The steam entering the cylinder of the preliminary throttle valve No. 6 causes the piston to move in the direction of arrow and opens valve No. 8, thus allowing the steam to pass into pipe (4) through choke No. 9 to the booster main steam-pipe (5). The choke No. 9 controls the quantity of steam, allowing sufficient for turning the booster over slowly.

While the foregoing is taking place, the steam is passing through pipe (3) to the clutch cylinder No. 7 and causing the clutch cylinder piston to move in direction of arrow, compressing spring No. 10, and by means of pin No. 11 moves idler gear rocker No. 12 on fulcrum No. 13, so that idler gear No. 14 meshes with axle gear No. 15. When the clutch cylinder piston has completed its movement, it uncovers port No. 16 and allows the steam to pass into pipe (7), seating ball No. 39 in by-pass valve No. 40, and thence to booster main throttle valve operating cylinder No. 17, and causes its piston to move in direction of arrow, thus opening the booster main throttle valve No. 18 and allowing the full steam pressure to be admitted from locomotive header to booster main steam-pipe (5).

When the steam pressure is built up in the booster main steam-pipe (5) the steam through pipe (8) enters the delay action valve No. 19, which controls the cylinder relief cock operating cylinder No. 20. The steam, on entering the delay action valve No. 19 causes the piston No. 21 to close the exhaust valve No. 22; the steam then passes slowly through needle-valve No. 23, and then through pipe (9) and builds up slowly behind the piston of the relief cock operating clyinder No. 20. When sufficient pressure has been built up to overcome the resistance of spring No. 24, the piston moves in the direction of arrow, and allows the steam in the booster cylinders to automatically shut off the cylinder drain cocks Nos. 25 and 26. A small hole in No. 27 is introduced in preliminary throttle valve No. 6; this is to permit a certain amount of steam being continually fed to booster cylinders, in order to keep them warm.

To idle the booster, the idling valve No. 28, shown in the reverse lever pilot valve No. 2, is turned so that the passage connects with the pipe (1) and allows the steam to flow direct to pipe (2) leading to the preliminary throttle valve and shutting it off from pipe (3) leading to clutch cylinder No. 7.

The exhaust from booster is taken through pipe (10) to the steam separator No. 29, and thence through pipe (11) into an annular space in blast-pipe No. 30 and to the atmosphere in the ordinary way. Valve No. 31 in the steam separator No. 29, which is balanced by counter-weight No. 32, is operated by the weight of trapped moisture in the chamber, the moisture being allowed to drain through the opening No. 33. The by-pass valve No. 40 is provided as an auxiliary exhaust from booster main throttle valve operating cylinder.

The booster cylinder sight-feed lubricator No. 41 is automatically started by steam from pipe (4) passing along pipe (14) from preliminary throttle valve, and is provided with an anti-syphoning device, No. 42, which breaks the syphoning action when steam is cut off by preliminary throttle valve.

CHAPTER VIII

Continuous Brakes—Details of Automatic Vacuum, Air-brake, Steam-brakes, Valves, etc.

General.

ALL passenger trains on British railways, as also a large number of fast goods trains, are equipped with continuous brakes, operated either by compressed air or vacuum. For the main line steam trains the automatic vacuum brake has been accepted, but for electric and rapid steam suburban services in congested areas the compressed air system is used, as a quicker release of the brakes can be effected. Vacuum brakes are standard in India, South America, South Africa, and on many Colonial railways, for both goods and passenger trains, but on the enormous railway system of North America, and also that of continental Europe, compressed air-brakes are used.

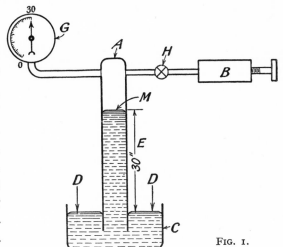

FIG. I.

In the case of the automatic vacuum brake, the power for operation is obtained by utilizing the pressure of the atmosphere exerted on suitable apparatus, partially exhausted by either a steam ejector or vacuum pump on the locomotive. The amount of pressure available will, of course, depend on the degree of exhaustion secured; a perfect vacuum at sea-level being equal to a pressure of 14·9 lbs. per sq. in., usually spoken of as 15 lbs., or the equivalent of a column of mercury 30 in. high. Fig. 1 will illustrate the elementary principles entailed. A is an upright tube about 40 in. long, of a bore equal to 1 sq. in., open at the bottom, where it dips into a supply of mercury, C. At the top it is closed and connected to a vacuum gauge, G, and a pump, or exhauster, B. If the pump is operated and the tube A partially exhausted, the atmosphere pressing on the surface of the mercury, DD, will force some of this up in proportion to the exhaustion secured. If a perfect vacuum could be secured then the mercury would rise to a maximum of nearly 30 in., E, or equal in weight to approximately 15 lbs.

The means of utilizing this pressure of the atmosphere to provide the necessary power for effective pressure on the brake-blocks to retard and stop a moving locomotive and train will now be explained.

Automatic Vacuum Brake.

The accompanying plate (Fig. 2), illustrates the arrangement of the automatic vacuum brake as applied to a locomotive, tender and carriage. It is simple, efficient, and its action will be readily understood from the plate. Briefly, as already noted, the operation of the automatic vacuum brake relies on the exhaustion of atmospheric air from the piping and cylinders throughout the train, and then the admission of air, either by accident or design, causes the brakes to be applied. Several modifications in the apparatus have been devised and used, but experience has dictated the form now generally adopted, which is that illustrated in the plate.

The apparatus is exhausted and the brake made effective by a large ejector on the locomotive, whilst the continuous vacuum required is maintained by either a small ejector, or—as now more usual—by an air-pump operated from one of the crossheads of the locomotive. With this latter a large steam ejector is also provided for the quick restoration of vacuum and release of the brakes after an application.

Ejectors.

One of the most powerful ejectors in regular use is shown by sections in Fig. 3. There are three views: (1) A longitudinal section of the ejector as arranged for being mounted externally to the boiler, and below it (2) a similar view through the body when the nozzles are arranged for internal application, and (3) a cross-section through the body and main air valve. The details are numbered and can be referred to in the accompanying schedule. Another form of ejector is given in Fig. 4, which has similar essential details, but is modified in the cones, solid nozzles being preferred to the annular ones, as in that illustrated in Fig. 3. The actual efficiency of these ejectors in service varies considerably, and naturally depends very much on the tightness of the brake apparatus, and its general condition. Roughly, they are capable of creating a vacuum of 23 to 25 in. on a " tight " locomotive and train, but herein, of course, it is necessary to take into consideration the number of vehicles—and, as aforesaid, their condition. An ejector working on a locomotive with normal boiler pressure of 150 lbs. per sq. in.,

TOMATIC BRAKE.

c manner the operation of the VACUUM

apparatus coloured ▢ are continuously

▨ are alternately under the influence of

g to the position occupied by the driver's

sphere when applying the brakes

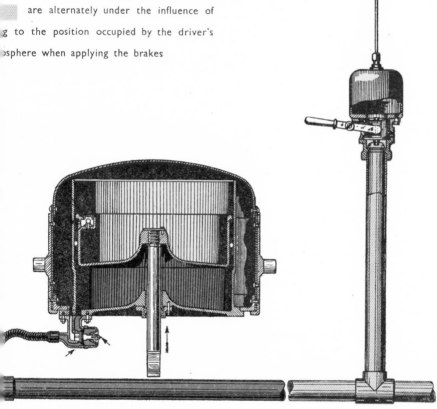

GUARDS VACUUM GAUGE

AIR ADMITTED TO TRAIN PIPE AND LOWER
PORTION OF CYLINDER—BRAKE ON

[To face page 168

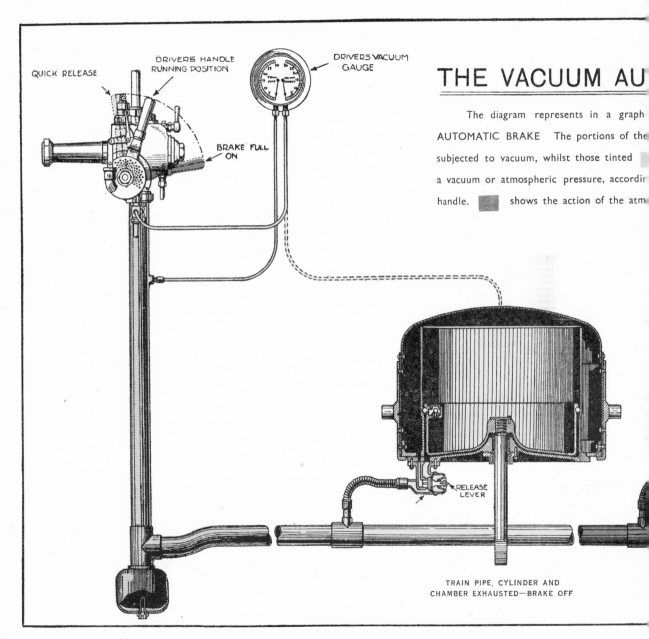

QUICK RELEASE

DRIVERS HANDLE
RUNNING POSITION

DRIVERS VACUUM
GAUGE

BRAKE FULL
ON

RELEASE
LEVER

TRAIN PIPE, CYLINDER AND
CHAMBER EXHAUSTED—BRAKE OFF

THE VACUUM AU

The diagram represents in a graph

AUTOMATIC BRAKE The portions of the

subjected to vacuum, whilst those tinted

a vacuum or atmospheric pressure, accordir

handle. shows the action of the atm

Fig. 2.

capable of creating 25 in. of vacuum on the locomotive, will probably
not produce more than 15 in. on a train of 40 to 50 vehicles (one
cylinder under each), in ordinary service condition.

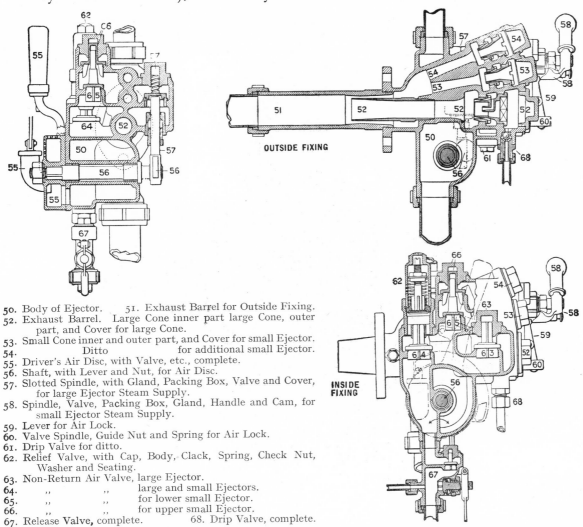

50. Body of Ejector.   51. Exhaust Barrel for Outside Fixing.
52. Exhaust Barrel. Large Cone inner part large Cone, outer
      part, and Cover for large Cone.
53. Small Cone inner and outer part, and Cover for small Ejector.
54.   Ditto   for additional small Ejector.
55. Driver's Air Disc, with Valve, etc., complete.
56. Shaft, with Lever and Nut, for Air Disc.
57. Slotted Spindle, with Gland, Packing Box, Valve and Cover,
      for large Ejector Steam Supply.
58. Spindle, Valve, Packing Box, Gland, Handle and Cam, for
      small Ejector Steam Supply.
59. Lever for Air Lock.
60. Valve Spindle, Guide Nut and Spring for Air Lock.
61. Drip Valve for ditto.
62. Relief Valve, with Cap, Body, Clack, Spring, Check Nut,
      Washer and Seating.
63. Non-Return Air Valve, large Ejector.
64.   ,,   ,,   large and small Ejectors.
65.   ,,   ,,   for lower small Ejector.
66.   ,,   ,,   for upper small Ejector.
67. Release Valve, complete.   68. Drip Valve, complete.

FIG. 3.—SUPER-DREADNOUGHT EJECTOR.

Brake Cylinders.

Fig. 5 gives a sectional view of one of the latest cylinders, with a
pressed steel body and chamber combined. When all the apparatus is
exhausted, air admitted from the train-pipe through the connecting
valve will cause pressure to exist under the piston, as the entry of air
is prevented above the piston by the action of the ball (Fig. 7) attached
to the cylinder. The piston will thus be forced up and the brake applied.
Re-exhausting the apparatus through the train-pipe will restore the

equilibrium in pressure, and the piston will fall, releasing the brakes. It will be noted in this case that the piston is rendered air-tight in the cylinder by a rolling ring of rubber.

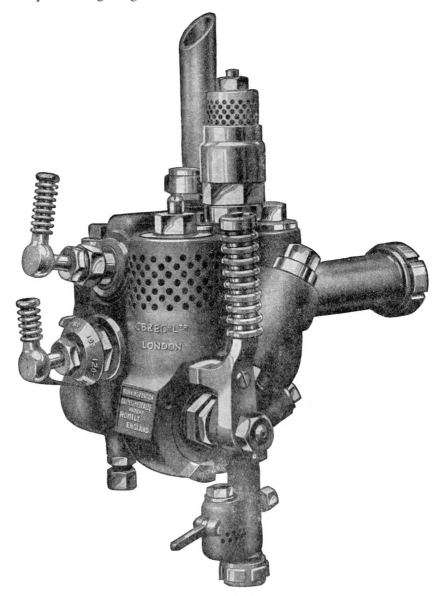

FIG. 4.—METCALFE'S IMPROVED EJECTOR.

Diaphragm Cylinder.

Another form of cylinder is shown in Fig. 6, wherein the rolling ring is replaced by a sheet-rubber diaphragm. In this case a separate reservoir, or chamber, is provided, to secure the necessary capacity above the

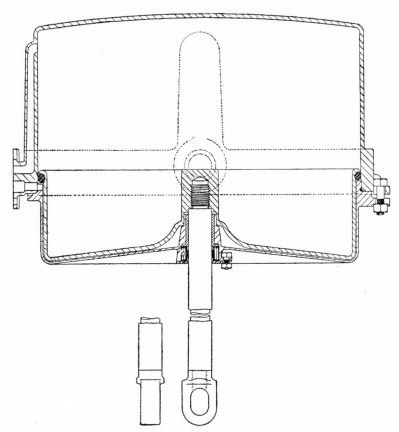

FIG. 5.—VACUUM BRAKE CYLINDER.

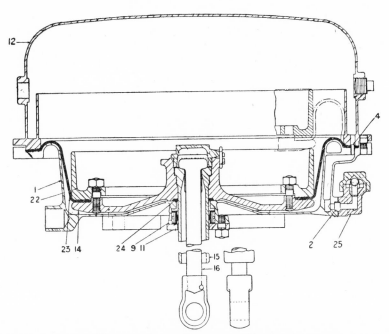

FIG. 6.—VACUUM BRAKE CYLINDER. (DIAPHRAGM TYPE.)

piston. The train-pipe and chamber pipe connections are shown on the left of the cylinder, the train-pipe being below. When vacuum is created, air is drawn from the top (chamber side of the cylinder), through the train-pipe connection and a passage at the back, 2 (it cannot be seen in the illustration), via the ball valve, through passages 2 and 4. When air is admitted through the train-pipe the ball valve will be seated and the piston pressed upwards. The diaphragm is of a rubber sheeting, reinforced with canvas insertion, and is good for some years in service. This cylinder being fixed rigidly to the locomotive framing, there is no need for flexible connecting pipes, with their disadvantages. Further, when the piston is at rest, its hub rests on the piston seat ring 24, and thus isolates the gland and eliminates any possible leakage from it into the train-pipe when running.

Referring to the illustration, 1 is the base; 12, the dome cover; 2 and 4, tubes for the ball valves and chamber passages respectively; 14, piston head; 22, piston follower; 15, piston trunk; 16, piston-rod; 20 and 21, piston-rod cap, with retaining split pin; 9 and 11, distance piece, packing and cap of gland; 23, diaphragm; 24, piston-seat ring; and 25, ball-valve case.

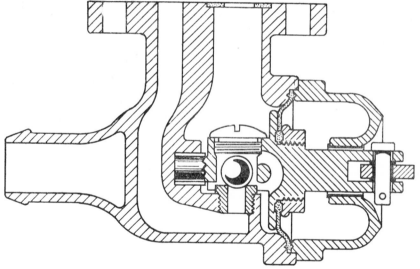

FIG. 7.—BALL AND RELEASE VALVE.

Ball Valve.

Fig. 7 shows in detail the ball valve, with release attachment, where it is contained in a separate fitting. Air is drawn from the train-pipe through the large passage to the left, past the inner side of the diaphragm, and from the chamber through the smaller passage. When air is admitted to the train-pipe to apply the brakes, it presses the ball valve on to its seat, thus isolating the chamber, etc., passes freely up the train-pipe and presses the piston up, applying the brakes. To release the brakes of a vehicle when vacuum cannot be restored, the valve spindle, which is connected up by cords to both sides of the vehicle, is pulled outward, which unseats the ball, admits air to the chamber and releases the brakes. Restoration of vacuum in the main train-pipe will cause atmospheric pressure on the outside of the diaphragm, press it inward and re-seat the ball.

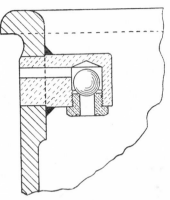

FIG. 8.—BALL VALVE IN PISTON.

There are a variety of forms of this ball valve, but all are similar in principle, except in those where the ball has been removed from this external attachment to the cylinder and placed inside the piston, so that it is away from any damage, cannot be easily removed —and, further, is thoroughly isolated for tightness. The detailed sketch, Fig. 8, will explain.

Other details requiring special mention are the couplings between the vehicles of the main train-pipe, illustrated in Fig. 9, which clearly shows the two adjacent ends, which are easily coupled up to form the continuous air-tight conduit required; and Fig. 10 gives the device termed the "van-valve," one of which is provided in each of the vans

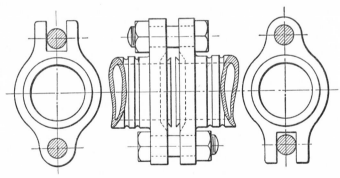

FIG. 9.—TRAIN PIPE COUPLING.

comprising a train. Its object is to give ready means for the guard to control the operation of the brake throughout the train, and also to secure quicker application of the brakes throughout the train in cases of emergency. This valve, as will be seen, has a vacuum chamber above it, which is exhausted through a small hole passing down the spindle. This acts as an exhausted chamber, which will ensure the valve being quickly opened in the case of sudden admission of air, for the underside of the diaphragm shown is always free to atmospheric pressure.

Owing to the large size of the cylinders needed for securing the brake pressure essential for a heavy locomotive, many engines are fitted with either steam- or air-brakes, these being arranged so that they will operate in conjunction with the train brakes.   To illustrate this, Fig. 11

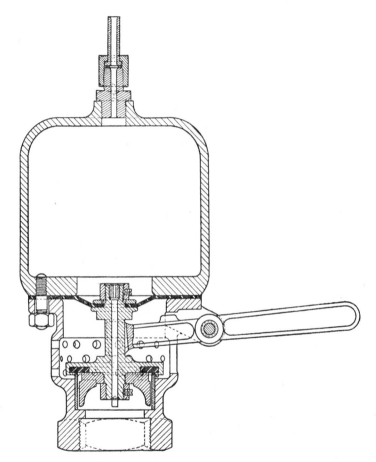

FIG. 10.—AUTOMATIC VAN VALVE.

is given.   In this arrangement one movement of the driver's handle controls both brakes, steam on the engine and vacuum on the train.

Driver's Valve.

The vacuum valve A is above, and the steam valve below the former, having a disc pattern inlet valve C, which revolves upon a face by movement of the driver's handle, letting in or keeping out air from the train-pipe, as required.   The steam-valve B is of the spindle type, with valves to suit the various parts. It controls the admission of steam to the brake cylinders and the escape of it for taking them off. Piston D is seen attached to the vacuum valve spindle, which is subject to the varying vacuum existing in the train-pipe. In moving outward it carries with it the lever E, opening the steam-brake valve spindle F, and allowing steam to pass the valve G to the brake cylinder. When vacuum is re-created to the requisite figure in the train-pipe by the ejector on the

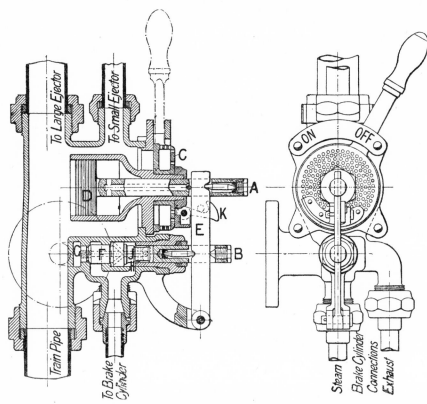

FIG. 11.—COMBINED VALVE, STEAM-BRAKE AND VACUUM.

engine, the piston D is drawn inward, the lever E closes valve G and opens the exhaust passage H, so that the steam in the cylinder is released. The ports shown at J in dotted lines through the spindle F are provided to permit any steam that may pass by valve G to escape freely out of the exhaust pipe, so preventing it from accumulating and applying the brake. The hook K is fitted to be engaged with a pin on the lever E to hold the steam-valve shut when the vacuum brake is not in use. The creation of vacuum in the train-pipe will automatically free this by the fact that piston D will move forward and the hook K drop by gravity.

Steam-brake Cylinders.

Figs. 12 and 13 show accepted forms of steam-brake for a locomotive. Fig. 12 is placed horizontally, the brakes being applied by piston *b*,

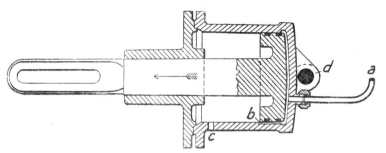

FIG. 12.—HORIZONTAL STEAM-BRAKE CYLINDER.

which is forced outward by steam entering through pipe *a*. Release is effected by springs arranged in the brake gear. Groove *b* and small hole *c* are provided for the escape of condensed steam.

Fig. 13 gives a vertical cylinder, with a trunk piston-rod containing a connecting link to the brake shaft. In this case the brakes are applied by admitting steam through pipe *a*, which forces the piston up and applies the brakes, which are ultimately released by springs. This arrangement is much used where the brakes of the engine and tender are operated by one cylinder on the engine. In this case any condensed steam escapes at *b*.

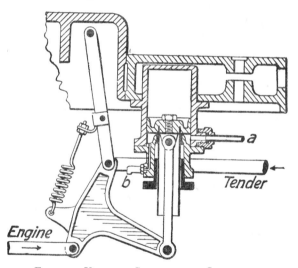

FIG. 13.—VERTICAL STEAM-BRAKE CYLINDER.

Brake Gear.

In the arrangement of the brake gear, or "rigging," as it is termed, it is very necessary that all rods should be as far as possible in tension, and only in exceptional cases in compression; when these do occur it is expedient that they be as heavy and as short as possible. Simplicity in the fitting of the pull-rods and levers is important, and all should be so arranged that they can be readily adjusted or taken down for replacement. Brake-blocks frequently need renewal, and when this is done they should, if possible, be replaced in pairs, so that the pressure is equally applied on both sides of an axle. As already mentioned, when referring to tender arrangement, all gear should be automatically equalized out so that the strains throughout the system are as uniform as possible.

Fig. 14 illustrates this, showing where pressure produced by a steam cylinder is equally distributed throughout the system applied to the

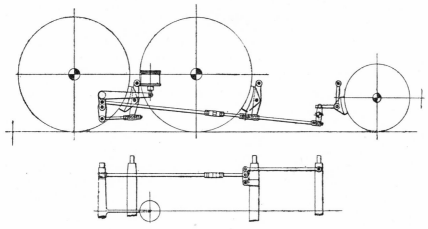

FIG. 14.—BRAKE ARRANGEMENT FOR 0-4-2 LOCOMOTIVE.

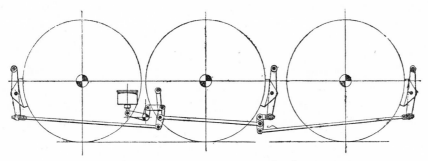

FIG. 15.—BRAKE ARRANGEMENT FOR 0-6-0 LOCOMOTIVE.

driving wheels and a trailing pair of carrying wheels. Fig. 15 gives another equalized system, applied to the six-coupled wheels of a goods locomotive.

Continuous Brakes on Long Trains.

The comparative merits of compressed air or vacuum have been much debated, and each has its advocates. As before stated, the vacuum system has been generally adopted in this country for use on both passenger and goods trains, and as it is also standard in India, South Africa, South America, etc., the following notes on its application to long trains may be of service, although regarding length the longest of trains fitted cannot equal those operated by compressed air in America. Whereas with the compressed air apparatus power exists on each vehicle to either apply or release the power, with the vacuum it only exists for application. To re-create vacuum for release, the engine ejector must be operated, and it takes time to exhaust the cylinders and piping of a long train.

Thirty-five to forty cylinders operating, or eighteen to twenty passenger coaches having two cylinders each, are considered the practical limit in service for ensuring quick release. In India as many as one hundred wagons are coupled up, but under these conditions the speed of release and degree of vacuum maintained are jeopardized.

To investigate the action of the vacuum brake on very long trains, experiments have been made with one hundred vehicles equipped with supplemental accelerator valves—shown in Fig. 16. With such valves and a train vacuum of 16 in., stoppages of a goods train of one hundred vans, running at 30 miles per hour, have been made in approximately the same distance as an express passenger train of ordinary formation at forty miles per hour. The

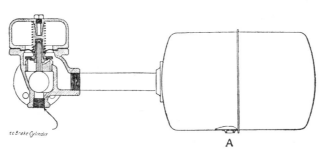

FIG. 16.—ACCELERATOR VALVE.

time occupied in re-creating vacuum throughout such a train was found to be considerable, and to prevent delay it is customary with freight trains to make an initial large reduction of vacuum to check the speed, and then to allow the small ejector or pump to slowly re-create and bring the vacuum back to normal by the time the train has come to a stand; it will then be almost ready to start away again. In cases where the vacuum becomes totally destroyed, as in attaching and detaching wagons, the time taken to re-create vacuum throughout a train may cause delay, but careful manipulation in the working will reduce this risk. With a 100-van train working with a 16-in. vacuum, it requires about $3\frac{1}{2}$ minutes to fully release the brakes, and $4\frac{1}{2}$ minutes to re-create the 16-in. vacuum through to the rear of the train; to secure a 20-in. vacuum it will require $7\frac{1}{2}$ minutes. These figures show the necessity for careful manipulation of the vacuum brake on long goods trains. Attempts are still being made to improve the speed of release, but the low pressure at which the apparatus works does not conduce to an easy solution of the problem.

The use of a reciprocating vacuum-pump driven from the crosshead of the locomotive has been mentioned as being used on some railways for the maintenance of the continuous vacuum required to keep the automatic feature of the brake in operation. The locomotive shown in the frontispiece is fitted with such a pump, as can be seen on reference to the drawing. Fig. 17 shows such a pump in detail. The suction port is seen just above the cylinder barrel. At either end of the port, and directly above it, are the suction valves, and above these the delivery valves. Near the left-hand set of valves is the train-pipe connection,

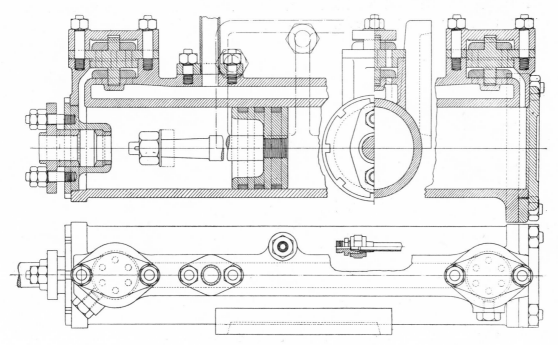

FIG. 17.—VACUUM-PUMP FOR LOCOMOTIVE.

and at the opposite end the vacuum reducing valve (not shown). The piston head is of cast-iron, with three cast-iron rings, whilst the gland of the piston-rod is shown for ordinary asbestos packing. In the latest forms, white metal packing-rings are used, and the piston has four narrow piston-rings instead of three wide ones.

Compressed Air-brakes.

In these the operating medium is air under pressure secured by a steam compressor on the engine, this providing a supply (usually) at 100 lbs. per sq. in. This pressure is reduced to 80 lbs. per sq. in. as it passes into the main train-pipe, which runs throughout the train. Under each vehicle there is a brake cylinder, a reservoir, and a triple valve,

Fig. 18. The function of the latter is important, for it controls the operation of the brake apparatus under the vehicle. Application of pressure throughout the train-pipe[1] moves the triple valves to such a position that the brake cylinders are connected with the atmosphere and the train-pipe is in communication with the reservoir, so that pressure is being stored there to the pre-determined maximum carried in the train-pipe. If the pressure in this latter pipe is reduced either by the design of the driver (or guard) or by accident (as the severance of the train-pipe) air will escape, train-pipe pressure fall, and the triple valve be moved into such a position that there will be a connection between the reservoir and the brake cylinder, enabling air to enter, push out

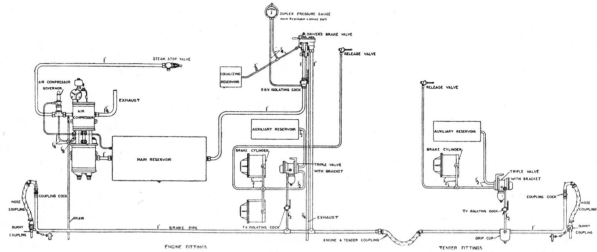

Fig. 18.—Diagrammatic arrangement of Westinghouse Automatic Brake apparatus on Engine and Tender.

the pistons and apply the brakes. Release is accomplished by restoring the pressure in the train-pipe, moving triple valves, opening the cylinders to exhaust and restoring the connection between train-pipe and reservoir.

From the above brief outline of operation it will be seen that the elements of very quick application and equally quick release are present, offering the more satisfactory service for electric, as well as rapid steam suburban passenger trains; there is also more energetic action for long goods trains. In the case of the latter, one hundred vehicles are common, and, although the operation throughout may not always be as smooth as it is with the lower pressure vacuum brakes, the period to secure rapid manipulation is of primary importance and has much to do with the preference it has received on railways like those of Canada, Australia,

[1] Sometimes referred to as Brake-pipe.

ING TRUCK.

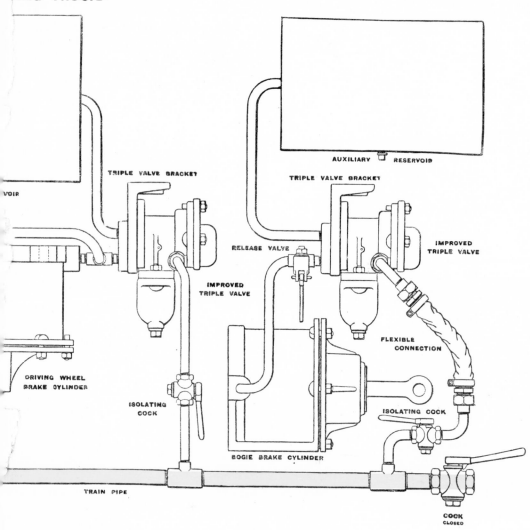

the main reservoir to the train-pipe. This restores the pressure in the train-pipe and returns the triple valves to their original position. In this position the slide valves of the triple valves allow e cylinders to escape to the atmosphere, so that the brake blocks are relieved of pressure and the are at the same time recharged from the train-pipe.

[*To face page* 180

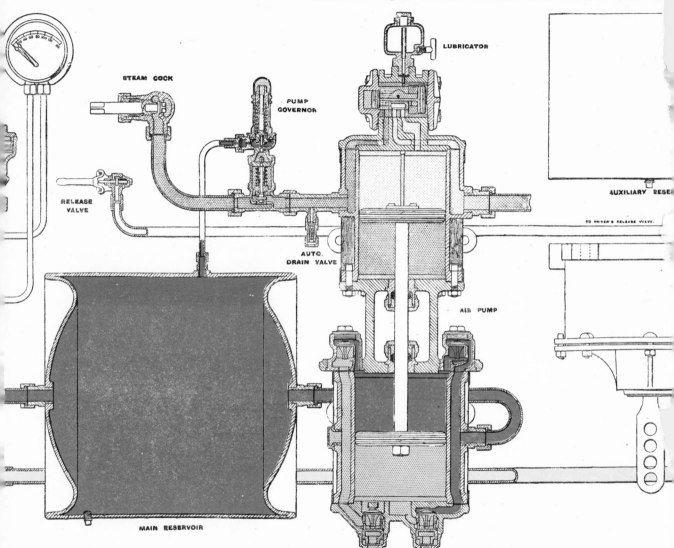

STEAM COCK

PUMP GOVERNOR

LUBRICATOR

RELEASE VALVE

AUTO. DRAIN VALVE

AIR PUMP

AUXILIARY RESE

TO DRIVER'S RELEASE VALVE.

MAIN RESERVOIR

AUTOMATIC AIR-BRAKE APPARATUS.

of an essential part of the apparatus should occur on any vehicle. The reduction of pressure in the train-
s the pistons of all the triple valves to move, and permits a portion of the compressed air stored in the
reservoirs to be instantly discharged into the brake cylinders. This air forces the pistons forward, pressing
-blocks against the wheels by means of the gear connected to the piston-rod. The brake force thus
corresponds with the reduction of pressure made in the train-pipe, consequently the action of the brake
aduated at will. The brakes are released by an increase of pressure in the main pipe, produced by

admitting air from
pistons of all the
the air in the bra
auxiliary reservoir

TENDER EQUIPMENT.

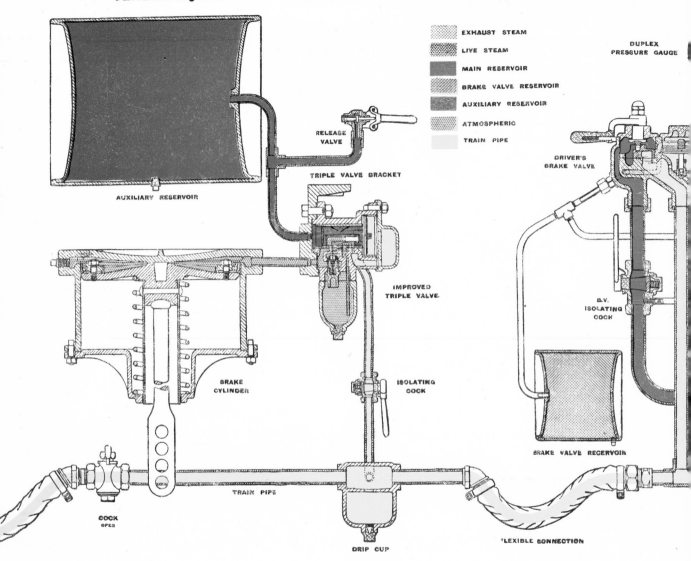

EXHAUST STEAM
LIVE STEAM
MAIN RESERVOIR
BRAKE VALVE RESERVOIR
AUXILIARY RESERVOIR
ATMOSPHERIC
TRAIN PIPE

DUPLEX PRESSURE GAUGE

RELEASE VALVE

TRIPLE VALVE BRACKET

IMPROVED TRIPLE VALVE

AUXILIARY RESERVOIR

DRIVER'S BRAKE VALVE

B.V. ISOLATING COCK

BRAKE CYLINDER

ISOLATING COCK

BRAKE VALVE RESERVOIR

COCK OPEN

TRAIN PIPE

DRIP CUP

FLEXIBLE CONNECTION

FIG. 19.—GENERAL ARRANGEMENT OF WESTINGHOUSE CONTINUOUS

be 70 lbs. per sq. inch, or any higher pressure which may be adopted for normal working. This pressure is automatically maintained by means of the feed-valve attached to the driver's brake valve, but there is no compressed air in the brake cylinders so long as the brake is not in operation.

The brakes are applied to all the vehicles on the train by a reduction of pressure purposely or accidentally produced in the system. In ordinary working this is effected by allowing air to escape to the atmosphere by the driver's brake valve or by the guard's emergency valve, but the same result follows if the train should part or if

a rupture
pipe caus
auxiliary
the brake
produced
can be g

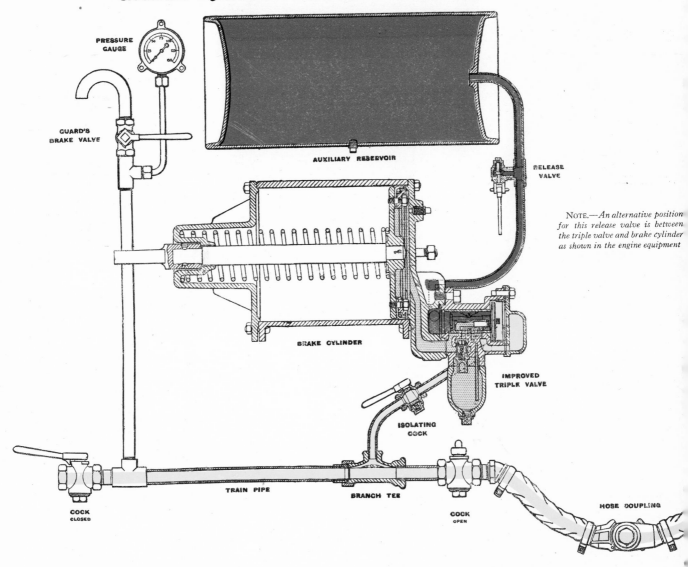

PRESSURE GAUGE

GUARD'S BRAKE VALVE

AUXILIARY RESERVOIR

RELEASE VALVE

NOTE.—*An alternative position for this release valve is between the triple valve and brake cylinder as shown in the engine equipment*

BRAKE CYLINDER

IMPROVED TRIPLE VALVE

ISOLATING COCK

COCK CLOSED

TRAIN PIPE

BRANCH TEE

COCK OPEN

HOSE COUPLING

METHOD OF OPERATION.—The air-pump, driven by steam from the boiler of the locomotive, compresses air to a pressure of from 90 to 100 lbs. per sq. inch in the main reservoir, which should have a capacity of from 12 to 15 cubic feet for ordinary passenger service, and a greater capacity for exceptionally heavy service.

When the locomotive is coupled to the train, the compressed air in the main reservoir is turned into the train-pipe, from which it passes through the branch pipes and fills the auxiliary reservoir on each vehicle. Thus the train-pipe, the triple valves, and the auxiliary reservoirs are all charged with an equal pressure of air, which should

etc. The plate, Fig. 19, shows the arrangement of apparatus in detail on a locomotive and carriage.

Non-automatic Air-brake.

The earliest form of the Westinghouse brake was the " Straight Air," or non-automatic brake, Fig. 20. Although this form of brake is not now used alone on trains, certain parts of the apparatus are common to it and the automatic brake.

In all forms of the Westinghouse brake the operating power is compressed air. The compressed air is admitted to one end of a brake cylinder. In the brake cylinder is a piston, one side of which is in direct connection with the atmosphere. The compressed air acts on the other side of the piston and forces it outwards. The motion of the

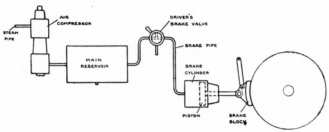

FIG. 20.—" STRAIGHT AIR " BRAKE ARRANGEMENT.

piston is transmitted by a suitable arrangement of levers to the brake-blocks, causing these to press against the wheels, and, by the consequent friction, to retard their motion.

The essential parts of the apparatus are therefore:

1. An air compressor to furnish a supply of compressed air.
2. A main reservoir to store the compressed air.
3. A driver's brake valve to control the movement of the compressed air into and out of the brake cylinder.
4. A brake-pipe to conduct the air from the compressor to the brake cylinder.
5. A brake cylinder and piston to transform the fluid pressure of the compressed air into mechanical force.
6. Levers, etc., to transmit the mechanical force from the brake cylinder to the brake-blocks.
7. Brake-blocks to be pressed against the wheels.

All the above parts were used in the non-automatic brake. The driver's brake valve consisted of a three-way cock by which compressed air was allowed to pass from the main reservoir to the brake cylinders to apply the brake, and from the brake cylinders to the atmosphere to release the brake. The driver could increase the pressure in the brake cylinders by allowing more air to pass into them, and could gradually decrease the pressure by allowing the air to escape.

This form of brake, however, had three great defects:

1. In the event of an accident to the brake-pipe, such as a burst hose coupling, or breaking in two of the train, all the compressed air would escape, and the brake would be useless.

2. The time required to apply or release the brake on trains of any considerable length was too great, because all the air used throughout the train in application and release of the brake had to pass through the driver's brake valve.

3. The braking power was too uneven, because, when applying the brake, the pressure in the brake cylinders at the front of the train was so much higher than in those at the rear.

Automatic Air-brake.

To overcome these defects, George Westinghouse, in 1872, invented the " Triple Valve," and by its use, along with an auxiliary reservoir on each vehicle, the brake was converted into an automatic brake. Since its introduction the triple valve has been modified, improved and amplified, but its fundamental parts and method of operation are still similar to those of the original type. Various types will be described later in detail, but, briefly, it may be said that the triple valve consists essentially of a cylindrical chamber C, Fig. 21, open at one end to the brake-pipe, and at the other to the auxiliary reservoir. This chamber contains a piston P, to the stem of which a slide-valve, SV, is attached. The slide-valve moves over a face in which there are two ports, one leading to the brake cylinder, and the other to the atmosphere.

Triple Valve.

The compressed air enters the cylindrical chamber from the train-pipe and forces the piston to the opposite end of the chamber, as in Fig. 21. Air then passes by a groove G in the wall of the chamber to the auxiliary reservoir, which is filled with air at the same pressure as the train-pipe. To apply the brake the driver reduces the pressure of air in the train-pipe by allowing some air to escape from the pipe to the atmosphere. The compressed air in the auxiliary reservoir is then at a higher pressure than the air remaining in the train-pipe, and therefore forces the triple valve piston P back towards the right-hand end of the chamber C (Fig. 22). This blanks off the groove G, cutting off communication between the train-pipe and auxiliary reservoir. The slide-valve SV being attached to the piston, moves with it, and first cuts off communication between the brake cylinder and atmosphere, and then uncovers the port leading to the brake cylinder, allowing the compressed air from the auxiliary reservoir to flow into the brake cylinder and apply the brake.

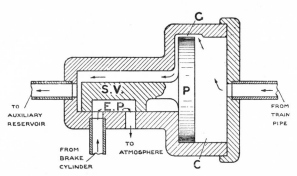

FIG. 21.—TRIPLE VALVE, BRAKE RELEASED.

To release the brake the driver increases the pressure in the train-pipe, by allowing compressed air from the main reservoir on the engine to enter it. The train-pipe pressure being now greater than that of the auxiliary, the triple valve piston is again moved towards the left, carrying the slide-valve with it. The exhaust port EP in the slide-valve then connects the port leading from the brake cylinder to that leading to the atmosphere. The compressed air in the brake cylinder then escapes to the atmosphere, and the brake is released. At the same time the auxiliary reservoir is re-charged with compressed air from the train-pipe through the groove G.

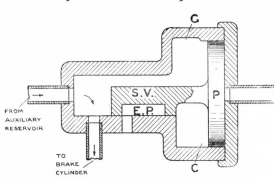

FIG. 22.—TRIPLE VALVE, BRAKE APPLIED.

It will be seen that any reduction of pressure in the train-pipe causes the brake to be applied. The brake is therefore automatic, because it will operate automatically in the case of an accident to the train-pipe—burst hose, broken coupling, etc.—and it can be applied from any part of the train by allowing air to escape from the train-pipe. Further, the time required to operate the brake is decreased, because the air used to apply the brake has only to pass from the auxiliary reservoir to the brake cylinder, and from the brake cylinder to the exhaust port of the triple valve to release it, instead of having to travel from and to the driver's brake valve, as in the case of the "non-automatic brake." The inequality in the braking action is also lessened because the air in the various auxiliary reservoirs, being at approximately the same pressure, corresponding pressure is obtained in the brake cylinders.

The automatic brake, as at first introduced, served very well while trains were comparatively short and light, and speeds low, but as these increased it was found that the time required to apply the brakes on the rear cars was too great, particularly in emergency. This was due to the fact that in an application of the brake all the air allowed to escape from the brake-pipe had to pass through the driver's brake valve, and, consequently, the longer the train, the longer the time required to apply the brakes at the rear. The brakes on the front cars were therefore applied some time in advance of these in the rear, resulting in the rear cars closing up on to those in front and causing shocks.

Quick-acting Triple Valve.

To remedy this, Mr. Westinghouse, in 1887, invented the " Quick-Acting Triple Valve." This triple valve was identical with the triple valve already described so far as ordinary or " service " applications of the brake were concerned, but in " emergency " applications, when a sudden reduction in train-pipe pressure is made at any part of the train, the piston and slide-valve of the triple valve nearest to the point where the reduction commenced travels to a position, not reached in " service " applications, and in this position air is allowed to escape direct from the brake-pipe to the brake cylinder, as well as from the auxiliary reservoir. The sudden reduction of train-pipe pressure causes the next triple valve in the train to operate in a similar manner, and so on throughout the train. The time of full application of the brakes on a fifty-car train is thereby reduced to about one-sixth of the time required with the ordinary triple valve, and the shocks formerly experienced are correspondingly lessened, and the stops shortened.

Many other improvements have since been made in the apparatus, and special types of apparatus have been designed to meet the varying requirements of express passenger trains, goods trains, electrically driven trains, etc.

Single-stage Air Compressor.

When steam is admitted to the compressor, Fig. 23, it enters the steam cylinder at A, flows through the passages B and C into the main valve chamber D of the top head, and passes also through the port J in to the reversing valve chamber R. The chambers D and R, therefore, always contain live steam of the same pressure.

The ports E and F, leading from the main valve chamber D to the ends of the steam cylinder 61, are opened for the admission and exhaust of steam by the movements of the slide-valve 71, which is attached to the stem of the main valve 68. The latter valve consists of two pistons of different diameters, forming the two ends of the same rod. The outer face of the larger piston is exposed to the pressure of steam, which is admitted to and discharged from the chamber K by the reversing valve 65. The space L at the opposite end of the main valve 68 communicates with the steam exhaust passage G by a small port (not illustrated), and hence is in communication with the atmosphere.

In the position of the ports shown, live steam is flowing from the main valve chamber D through the passage F to the lower end of the cylinder 61, forcing the steam-piston 77 upwards, while the steam previously admitted to the opposite end of the cylinder will exhaust into the atmosphere through the ports E, G and H.

When the steam-piston 77 has nearly completed its upward stroke, the reversing plate 81 presses against the shoulder of the rod 83, and raises the rod with the reversing valve 65. The valve then first cuts off the communication between the port N and the exhaust passage M, and by its further movement opens the port P, through which live steam flows to the space K at the right-hand side of the main valve 68. The steam thus admitted balances the pressure on the opposite side of the larger main valve piston, and the pressure, acting on the inner surface of the smaller piston, moves the main valve 68 with the slide-valve 71 towards the left. Steam from the main valve chamber D then flows through the port E to the upper end of the steam cylinder 61, forcing

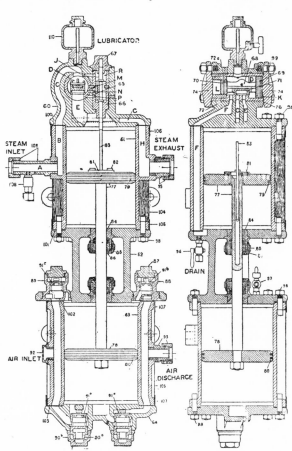

FIG. 23.—SINGLE-STAGE AIR COMPRESSOR.

the main piston 77 downwards, whilst the steam from the opposite end of the cylinder escapes through the ports F, G and H into the atmosphere.

When the steam-piston approaches the end of its down stroke, the reversing plate 81 presses against the button at the end of rod 83, thus drawing down the latter and the reversing valve 65. The cavity in this valve then again connects the ports M and N, through which the steam from the space K at the right-hand side of the main valve 68 flows to the exhaust port G, and hence through the chamber H into the atmosphere. The outer faces of the two main valve pistons are now both relieved of pressure, whilst their inner faces are exposed to the pressure of the live steam contained in the chamber D between them. As the piston on the right has a larger area than that on the opposite side, the main valve 68 is moved to the right, into the position represented by the illustration. The slide-valve 71 then uncovers port F, thus again admitting steam to the lower end of the cylinder 61, and allowing the steam from the upper end to escape through the ports E and G into the atmosphere.

The air-piston 78 on its upward stroke inhales air at atmospheric pressure through the strainer 92 and suction valve 91a into the bottom part of the cylinder 63. At the same time air previously drawn into the top part of the cylinder is compressed, and delivered by way of delivery valve 91b, to the passage leading to the discharge pipe, and thence to the main air reservoir. At each downward stroke of the piston, the air already in the bottom part of the cylinder is compressed and discharged through delivery valve 91d, and a fresh supply of air at atmospheric pressure is drawn into the top part of the cylinder 63, by way of suction strainer 92 and suction valve 91c, to be compressed and delivered in the return stroke, as already described.

Driver's Brake Valve.

The valve generally used now to operate the automatic brake is known as " No. 4, Driver's Brake Valve." With this valve, Fig. 24, there is used a small reservoir termed the " equalizing reservoir," of which the purpose will be explained.

Fig. 25 shows the ports and recesses in the body, and Fig. 25A those in the main valve.

There are five principal positions of the valve handle for working the brake.

I. *Position for Charging the Train and Releasing the Brakes.*—When the valve handle 6 is placed in this position, compressed air from the main reservoir, entering the brake valve at F, flows through the ports *a* and *b*, the cavity *i* (in the rotary valve 4), and through the ports *e* and K (in the valve body 1), to the passage L, whence it passes to the chamber T, seating the equalizing piston 11, and also feeds into the small reservoir attached to the brake valve.

At the same time, compressed air from the main reservoir also flows through the port *a* of the rotary main valve 4 into a blank cavity H in the body 1. This, in the present position of the valve, communicates with the cavity S in the valve face, and allows the air to pass through S into the port V, and the brake-pipe E. Thus a direct and free communication is established from the main reservoir to the brake-pipe, as well as to the chamber T and the small reservoir attached to it. The

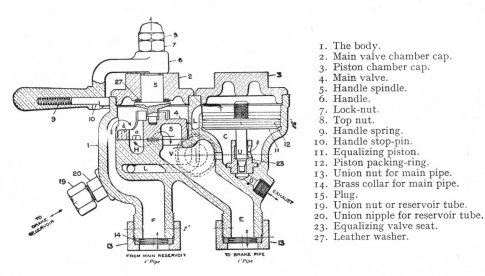

1. The body.
2. Main valve chamber cap.
3. Piston chamber cap.
4. Main valve.
5. Handle spindle.
6. Handle.
7. Lock-nut.
8. Top nut.
9. Handle spring.
10. Handle stop-pin.
11. Equalizing piston.
12. Piston packing-ring.
13. Union nut for main pipe.
14. Brass collar for main pipe.
15. Plug.
19. Union nut or reservoir tube.
20. Union nipple for reservoir tube.
23. Equalizing valve seat.
27. Leather washer.

FIG. 24.—DRIVER'S VALVE.

exhaust valve U closes the port O, and equal pressure exists on both side of the piston 11.

II. *Position whilst Running.*—When the valve handle is turned into the second position, the air flowing through the passage *a* of the rotary valve, feeds into the cavity H in the valve seat, but can no longer pass to the brake-pipe E, as the communication between the cavities H and S is now cut off. From the port V air passes through the cavity S and the port *d* in the body to the passage L and chamber T, thus equalizing the pressure above and below piston 11. In this position, however, the port *b* in the rotary main valve 4 corresponds with port *c* in the body 1, leading to the attached feed-valve.

III. *Lap Position.*—When the valve handle is placed in this position, all ports in the rotary valve 4, as well as in its seat, are closed, and all communication to and from the brake-pipe E, the chamber T, and the brake-valve reservoir, is cut off.

IV. *Position for Moderate Applications of the Brake.*—To apply the brake with moderate force, the valve handle is turned to the position IV, when air from the chamber T and its reservoir is allowed to escape into the atmosphere through the passage L and port *e* in the body 1, the recess *f* in the rotary valve, and the exhaust opening W in the valve seat. This causes a reduction of pressure on the top of the piston 11; the excess of pressure now acting on the under side of this piston forces it upwards, unseating the discharge valve U, and allowing air to escape from the brake-pipe E, through the exhaust port O, until the pressure in the pipe throughout the train is equal to that yet remaining in the

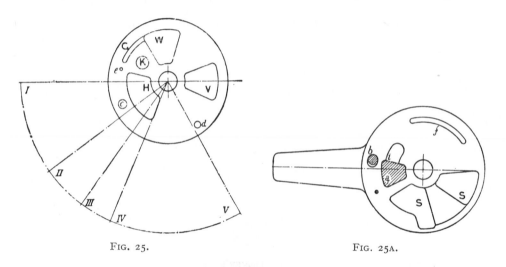

FIG. 25.　　　　　　　　　　FIG. 25A.

chamber T. When equilibrium of pressure is thus established, the piston is moved back, and the valve U returned to its seat, closing the exhaust port O, and preventing further escape of air.

V. *Position for Emergency Applications of the Brake.*—When the valve handle is turned beyond the position IV towards the right, a wide and direct communication between the brake-pipe and the atmosphere is established through the port V, the cavity S in the rotary valve 4, and the exhaust opening W in the seat of that valve; the air, therefore, escapes from the main pipe E with great rapidity, causing instantaneous application of all the brakes with full power.

Ordinary Triple Valve.

The construction and mode of operation of this valve, Fig. 26, are as follows: Enclosed in a case 1 is a piston 5, carrying with it a slide-valve 6, which covers the port *a* to the brake cylinder, and in the position shown establishes a communication between port *a* and the atmosphere by the cavity *b* and exhaust passage *c*. Compressed air from the brake-pipe enters at E, and forcing up the piston 5, feeds past it through the groove *d* and passage C into the auxiliary reservoir, which is thus charged with an air-pressure equal to that in the brake-pipe. The reservoir, triple valve and brake-pipe then contain equal air-pressure, and so long as this is maintained, the brake remains out of operation.

Upon a reduction of pressure being made in the brake-pipe, the piston 5 will be moved downwards, owing to the excess of pressure now acting on its upper surface. The piston—having a limited movement

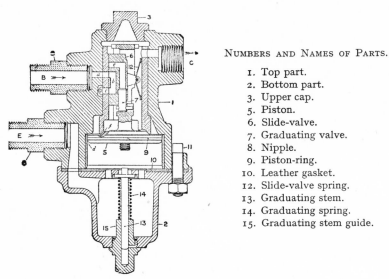

NUMBERS AND NAMES OF PARTS.

1. Top part.
2. Bottom part.
3. Upper cap.
5. Piston.
6. Slide-valve.
7. Graduating valve.
8. Nipple.
9. Piston-ring.
10. Leather gasket.
12. Slide-valve spring.
13. Graduating stem.
14. Graduating spring.
15. Graduating stem guide.

FIG. 26.—TRIPLE VALVE.

without affecting the slide-valve 6—closes the feed-groove *d*, at the same time unseating the graduating valve 7, which thus opens the port *e*. The piston then also moves downwards the slide-valve 6, which cuts off the communication from the cylinder to the exhaust port *c*, and opens the port *e* to the passage *a* leading to the brake cylinder, into which compressed air from the auxiliary reservoir immediately flows and applies the brake. The further downward movement of the piston 5 and slide-valve 6 is arrested by the decrease of pressure above the piston, caused by the air flowing into the brake cylinder. So soon as the pressure in the reservoir is thus reduced a little below that in the brake-pipe, the piston 5 is moved up so far that it closes the graduating valve 7, while the slide-valve 6 retains its position. By simply producing further reductions of pressure in the brake-pipe, the motion of the piston 5 and graduating valve 7, may be repeated, and the driver can thus gradually introduce any desired pressure into the brake cylinder from zero up to the full power.

When a considerable reduction of pressure in the brake-pipe is suddenly made, the piston 5 is at once forced down to the limit of its stroke, and seated on the leather gasket 10. The slide-valve 6 then entirely uncovers the port *a*, so that the compressed air from the auxiliary

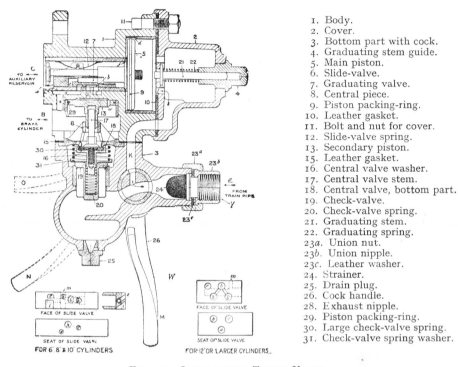

1. Body.
2. Cover.
3. Bottom part with cock.
4. Graduating stem guide.
5. Main piston.
6. Slide-valve.
7. Graduating valve.
8. Central piece.
9. Piston packing-ring.
10. Leather gasket.
11. Bolt and nut for cover.
12. Slide-valve spring.
13. Secondary piston.
15. Leather gasket.
16. Central valve washer.
17. Central valve stem.
18. Central valve, bottom part.
19. Check-valve.
20. Check-valve spring.
21. Graduating stem.
22. Graduating spring.
23*a*. Union nut.
23*b*. Union nipple.
23*c*. Leather washer.
24. Strainer.
25. Drain plug.
26. Cock handle.
28. Exhaust nipple.
29. Piston packing-ring.
30. Large check-valve spring.
31. Check-valve spring washer.

FIG. 27.—QUICK-ACTING TRIPLE VALVE.

reservoir flows into the brake cylinder with great rapidity, applying the brake with full force.

To release the brake, air is again admitted from the main reservoir to the brake-pipe. The air-pressure, acting against the reduced pressure in the auxiliary reservoir, forces the piston 5 and slide-valve 6 back into the positions shown in the figure, thus permitting the air in the brake cylinder to exhaust through the port *c*, whilst at the same time the auxiliary reservoir is re-charged through the feed-groove *d*.

Quick-acting Triple Valve.

This device consists of two piston valves, one working horizontally and the other vertically, Fig. 27.

In ordinary applications of the brake, only the horizontal main piston valve operates, admitting air from the auxiliary reservoir into the brake cylinder, whilst the secondary piston 13 and the valve 18 remain at rest. When, however, on a sudden reduction of the pressure in the brake-pipe, the piston 5 and its slide-valve 6 are brought to their extreme position towards the right, compressed air is admitted to the upper side of the secondary piston 13, which, being driven down, opens the valve 18, thus admitting compressed air from the brake-pipe through the check-valve 19 to the brake cylinder, which at the same time is also charged with compressed air, admitted by the slide-valve 6, from the auxiliary reservoir. This discharge of air from the brake-pipe into the brake cylinders has the effect of reducing the pressure in the brake-pipe with great rapidity.

When compressed air from the main reservoir is admitted by means of the driver's valve into the brake-pipe to release the brakes, it enters the triple valve by the passages K and 1, and forces piston 5 and slide-valve 6 to their original position. In the course of this movement the exhaust cavity *b* of the slide-valve first connects the passage *h* to the exhaust port *c*, relieving the pressure from the top of the piston 13, which is returned to the position shown by the air pressure in the brake cylinder, whilst the spring 20 closes the valve 18. As the slide-valve 6 completes its leftward movement, the cavity *b* also opens the passage *a* to the exhaust port *c*, which discharges the air from the brake cylinder and releases the brakes. The auxiliary reservoir is again charged as before described, through the grooves *d* and *f*.

To secure the simultaneous release of the brakes, a nipple, having an aperture, the size of which depends upon the size of the brake cylinder with which the triple valve is used, is inserted in the mouth of the exhaust port.

By means of the cock in the lower part of the triple valve, the whole brake apparatus on a vehicle, or simply the quick-acting feature thereof, may be put out of use, without in any way affecting the action of the brakes on other vehicles of the same train. In position M of the cock-handle, the quick action is in use; in position N the brake is entirely put out of operation; whilst in position O, the quick action only is taken away, and the apparatus works in precisely the same manner as the " ordinary " triple valve.

Brake Cylinders.

A brake cylinder is fitted to every locomotive tender, and braked vehicle, Figs. 28 and 29.

Each brake cylinder contains a piston, having its rod attached to the brake gear in such a manner that the brake-blocks are pressed against the wheels when the piston is forced out by air pressure.

As long as the brake is not applied, the cylinder is free from air pressure. When, however, the brake is put into operation, compressed air is admitted to the cylinder by the corresponding triple valve, and the air pressure, acting upon the piston, forces the latter forward, thus applying the brake-blocks to the wheels. Upon the air being allowed to escape from the cylinder, the spring (which has been compressed in applying the brake) extends and returns the piston and brake gear to their original positions, thereby releasing the blocks from the wheels.

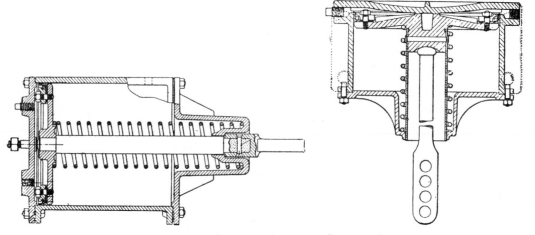

FIG. 28.—HORIZONTAL BRAKE CYLINDER.   FIG. 29.—VERTICAL BRAKE CYLINDER.

The cylinder shown in Fig. 29 is designed to operate with its piston-rod vertical. The piston-rod is a hollow sleeve or trunk, with a loose push-rod to which the lever of the brake shaft is attached, and this construction allows for the radial movement at the end of the brake shaft lever. When a hand-brake is fitted as well as the Westinghouse brake, the former can be applied without compressing the release spring in the brake cylinder, and an additional release spring of the type shown in Fig. 30 is provided on the brake gear to ensure that the brake-blocks fall clear of the wheels. Horizontal brake cylinders are provided with trunk pistons when required.

To prevent the application of the brake from slight leakage in the brake-pipe, each brake cylinder is provided with a small groove, which establishes a communication between both sides of the piston when the brake is applied. If, on account of such leakage, a slight flow of air to the brake cylinder should occur, the air would pass through the groove to the atmosphere without moving the piston. When, however, a considerable quantity of air is admitted to the cylinder, as in an ordinary application of the brake, the piston is immediately forced past the groove, and an escape of air from the cylinder is thus prevented.

In order to ensure that the pistons of all the brake cylinders in the train completely clear the corresponding leakage grooves, the driver should always reduce the pressure in the brake-pipe by not less than 5 lbs., whenever he puts the brake into operation, and care must also be taken that on every vehicle the brake gear is so adjusted that it allows the piston to travel sufficiently far.

Brake Rigging, etc.

In order to obtain the most efficient use of the power developed in the brake cylinder, it is necessary that the system of rods and levers by which that power is transmitted to the brake-blocks should be carefully designed and arranged. The position and proportions of these rods and levers with respect to each other must be such that the

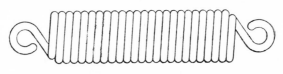

FIG. 30.—RELEASE SPRING.

rods exert the most effective pulls on the levers, free from any interference or unnecessary friction in any position. The power must be transmitted from the brake cylinders to the various brake-blocks, so that the desired pressure is obtained between each block and the wheel, and the strength of all the rigging must afford a high factor of safety above the maximum calculated stresses, while avoiding unnecessary spring or lost motion.

The ratio which the total pressure on the brake-blocks bears to the force exerted on the brake cylinder piston is termed " the leverage of the brake rigging "; e.g. if the former is 12,000 lbs. and the latter is 2000 lbs., the leverage is 6 : 1. It is recommended that the leverage should not exceed 8 : 1 with horizontal brake cylinders, or 6 : 1 with vertical brake cylinders, otherwise the wear of the blocks and pins, the spring of the rigging, and the movement of the axles in their bearings, etc., may increase the piston travel inordinately.

The pressure of the blocks against the wheels must be proportionate to the pressure between the wheels and the rails. The following have been found to be suitable proportions of brake-block pressure relative to weights on wheels:

Locomotive Driving and Trailing Wheels.—Sixty-five per cent. of the minimum weight on the braked wheels with the engine in working order. In the case of coupled wheels, if any such be not provided with brake-blocks, the remaining wheels should have the brake force required by the unbraked wheels in addition to their own.

Locomotive Bogie.—Fifty per cent. of the minimum weight on the wheels in working order.

Tender.—Eighty-five per cent. to 100 per cent. of the weight on the braked wheels when the tender is empty; *all wheels* should be braked.

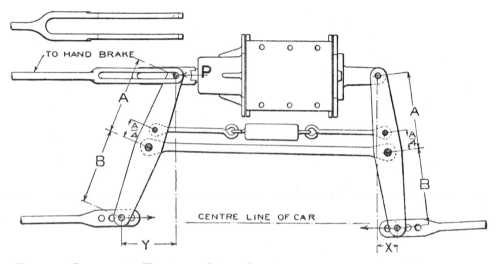

FIG. 30A.—LAY-OUT FOR HORIZONTAL LEVER GEAR, SHOWING CONNECTION TO HAND-BRAKE.

Passenger Carriage (including all vehicles run in passenger service).—Seventy-five per cent. of the weight on the braked wheels when the vehicle is empty; *all wheels* should be braked.

Freight Truck or Wagon.—Seventy per cent. to 75 per cent. of the weight on the wheels when the vehicle is empty.

Electric Traction.—For electric traction, where the energy of rotation of the armature geared to the axle must be destroyed, a larger brake percentage is recommended, depending upon circumstances. Usually 85 per cent. to 90 per cent.

Whenever possible, two brake-blocks should be used for each wheel, as this arrangement results in a higher coefficient of friction between the brake-blocks and wheel and less wear to the blocks, while the resultant pressure of the axle journal against its bearing during a brake application is centralized, instead of acting against one side of the journal, as in the case of the use of one block per wheel. When two brake-blocks are used per wheel the pressure on the two blocks should be equal.

The brake rigging should be designed to give equal pressure on all wheels arranged to carry equal loads, and this pressure should remain the same when the brake-blocks are unevenly worn.

All brake-blocks should be hung so that the centre of the block is slightly below the centre line of the wheel when the car is un-loaded, to prevent chattering. This will also reduce the danger of flat wheels. In all cases the brake-block levers should be so inclined that, when the brake is off, the blocks may fall by gravity, clear of the wheels.

The hand-brake should be so arranged as to pull on the brake cylinder crosshead pin or its lever, so that all levers will move in the same direction, whether the brake is applied by hand or air.

As the brake rigging consists of a system of levers and rods, the following points have to be borne in mind in calculating the necessary proportions of the levers required to develop the desired braking force on the wheel.

In the following diagrams:

The force P = area of the brake cylinder piston × maximum pressure available in the cylinder (usually taken as 50 lbs. per sq. in.);

W (shown as a weight acting on the lever) – pressure of the brake-block against the wheel produced by the force P acting on the lever in the direction of the arrow;

C is the fulcrum.

There are three kinds of levers with reference to the relative positions of the fulcrum C, force P, and the weight W, as shown below:

When the fulcrum C is between the force P and the weight W, force at C = W + P. (See Fig. 31.)

When the weight W is between the force P and the fulcrum C, force at C = W − P. (See Fig. 32.)

When the force P is between the weight W and the fulcrum C, force at C = P − W. (See Fig. 33.)

By substituting known forces or lengths for the letters used in the formulæ, unknown forces or lengths may be found, and the proper proportions of brake levers determined.

The brake gear may be arranged in many different ways to suit the construction of the various types of rolling-stock.

To obtain the most satisfactory action, the levers must be so arranged that they are at right angles to the centre line of the brake cylinder when the piston stands out at its medium stroke S, equal to 6 in., with brake cylinders having a maximum stroke of 12 in. To obtain this position,

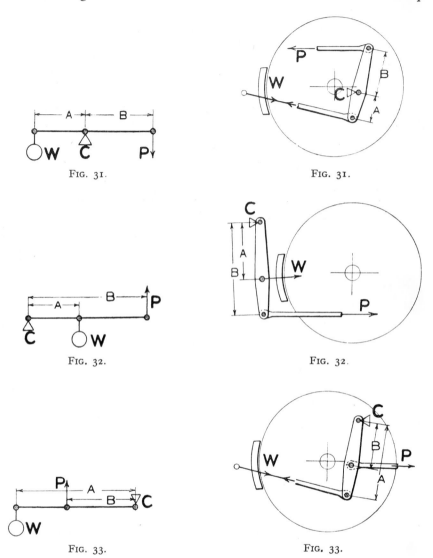

Fig. 31.   Fig. 31.

Fig. 32.   Fig. 32.

Fig. 33.   Fig. 33.

the distances X and Y (in inches) when the cylinder piston is fully released should be as follows:

$$X = \frac{B}{A} \times \frac{S}{2}; \quad Y = S + X = S + \left(\frac{B}{A} \times \frac{S}{2}\right).$$

Automatic Slack Adjuster.

For heavy suburban traffic, with its frequent stops and consequent rapid wear of the brake-blocks, and for vehicles on which the brake-gear is not readily accessible, an automatic slack adjuster can be used which automatically maintains a maximum predetermined piston travel. Any excess of this movement brings the adjusting mechanism into action and reduces the clearance between the block and the wheel, thereby reducing the piston travel on the next outward stroke of the piston. By this means the distance between the brake-blocks and the wheels on all the vehicles of a train is kept within certain limits throughout the life of the blocks, thus ensuring smooth stops and high working efficiency. Further, by the automatic adjustment of the slack, the brake-block can be worn to its utmost limit, and the air consumption reduced, thus effecting economy in both maintenance and running costs. The total leverage of the brake rigging when used with slack adjuster should not exceed 8 : 1.

Adjustment of Brake Gear.

With any kind of gear a considerable amount of brake force is lost when the levers assume unsuitable positions on account of the slack in the gear caused by the wear of the brake-shoes. It is therefore of great importance that ample provision should be made for the proper re-adjustment of the gear as the brake-shoes become worn. One means for this purpose is to provide the ends of connecting rods and truss-bars with a series

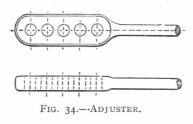

FIG. 34.—ADJUSTER.

of pinholes, as shown (Fig. 34). When the slack between the blocks and the wheel has become excessive it can be taken up by disconnecting the corresponding lever from the pull-rod and truss-bar, and pinning it to the adjoining set of holes, so that the blocks are drawn nearer together, whilst the vertical lever practically retains its original position.

Vacuum-operated Application Valve.

A common practice on British railways using vacuum brakes on the trains has been to equip the locomotives with steam-brakes arranged to operate through the medium of a suitable valve in conjunction with the continuous brakes of the train. This permits of smaller cylinders and more convenient details being used, an important consideration in the general arrangement of a modern high-powered locomotive built to the confined limits of the British loading-gauge.

A more useful and equally compact combination is to be found in the equipment of the locomotives with air-brake apparatus arranged to operate simultaneously with the vacuum brake on the train; such an installation further enables a fitted locomotive to be available for working quick suburban services, emergency haul of electric trains on which rapid acting air-brakes may be preferred, and, in addition, it provides the locomotive with auxiliary power for operating the reversing, sand and other gears requiring such, or controlling " boosters," etc.

The valve herewith illustrated has recently been introduced, and is understood to be giving satisfactory service, ensuring the application of the engine air-brakes, synchronizing with the vacuum on the train.

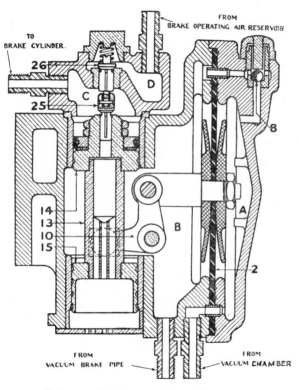

FIG. 35.—VACUUM-OPERATING VALVE FOR PROPORTIONAL APPLICATIONS.

The valve, Fig. 35, consists of a chamber in which a diaphragm operated on by vacuum is located, controlling an air-valve for admitting air to, or allowing it to exhaust from, the air-brake cylinders of the locomotive. The diaphragm is subjected to vacuum; on the side A it is in connection with the vacuum chamber, and on B with the train-pipe; a small ball check-valve 8 ensures the normal degree of vacuum being retained as existing in the train-pipe.

One arm of a bell-crank 10 is connected to the diaphragm 2, the other engaging with a hollow stem 13 joining two balancing pistons 14 and 15. The upper piston 14 carries a poppet valve 25, which controls the exhaust of air from the air-brake cylinder, with which the chamber C above this piston is in communication. The upper part of this chamber is closed by a valve 26, attached by a loose pin-joint to the exhaust valve 25, the valve 26 controlling the admission of air from the air reservoir (which is in communication with chamber D) to the brake cylinder.

When a vacuum brake application is made, the vacuum is partially, or wholly, destroyed in the brake-pipe and in the chamber B. The diaphragm is then forced to one side by the differential of the pressures acting on it, moving the bell-crank 10 and causing the balancing pistons

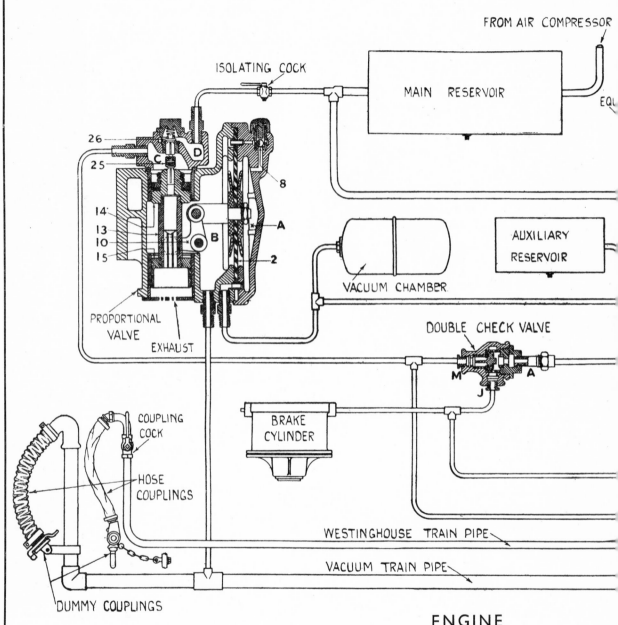

FROM AIR COMPRESSOR

ISOLATING COCK

MAIN RESERVOIR

EQU

26

25

C D

8

14

13

10

15

B

A

2

PROPORTIONAL VALVE

EXHAUST

VACUUM CHAMBER

AUXILIARY RESERVOIR

DOUBLE CHECK VALVE

M A

J

COUPLING COCK

BRAKE CYLINDER

HOSE COUPLINGS

WESTINGHOUSE TRAIN PIPE

VACUUM TRAIN PIPE

DUMMY COUPLINGS

ENGINE

WESTINGHOUSE AUTOMATIC AIR-BR

For names of parts of proportional valve,
see page 198.

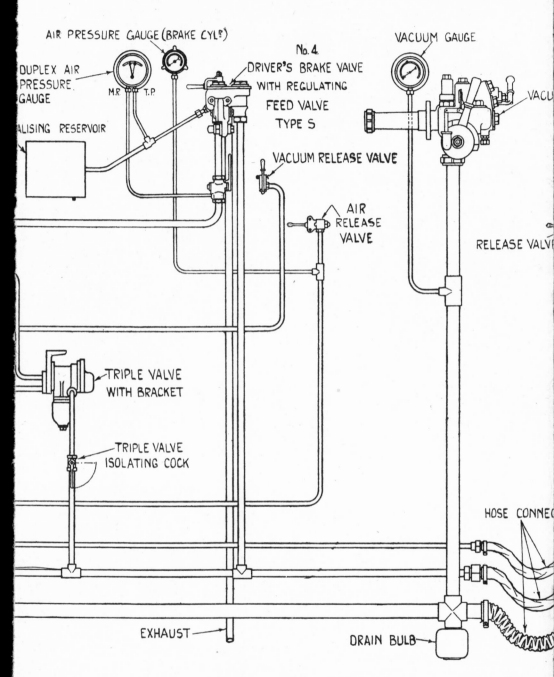

AIR PRESSURE GAUGE (BRAKE CYL.R)

DUPLEX AIR PRESSURE GAUGE

M.R.   T.P.

No. 4
DRIVER'S BRAKE VALVE
WITH REGULATING
FEED VALVE
TYPE S

VACUUM GAUGE

VACU

EQUALISING RESERVOIR

VACUUM RELEASE VALVE

AIR RELEASE VALVE

RELEASE VALVE

TRIPLE VALVE WITH BRACKET

TRIPLE VALVE ISOLATING COCK

HOSE CONNEC

EXHAUST

DRAIN BULB

RAKE ON ENGINE AND TENDER WITH PROPORTIONAL VALVE FOR O
AUTOMATIC VACUUM-BRAKE ON THE TRAIN

FIG. 35A.

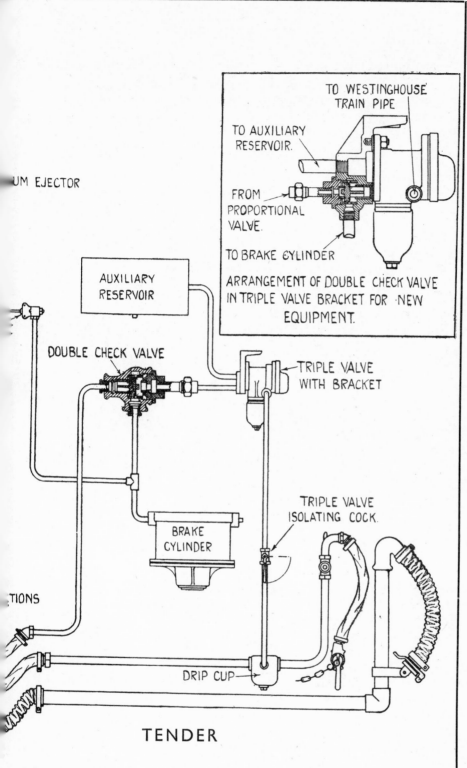

UM EJECTOR

TO WESTINGHOUSE TRAIN PIPE

TO AUXILIARY RESERVOIR.

FROM PROPORTIONAL VALVE.

TO BRAKE CYLINDER

ARRANGEMENT OF DOUBLE CHECK VALVE IN TRIPLE VALVE BRACKET FOR NEW EQUIPMENT.

AUXILIARY RESERVOIR

DOUBLE CHECK VALVE

TRIPLE VALVE WITH BRACKET

TRIPLE VALVE ISOLATING COCK.

BRAKE CYLINDER

:TIONS

DRIP CUP

TENDER

ERATING THE

14 and 15 to move upwards, first seating the exhaust valve 25, and then, in a further movement, opening the inlet valve 26 and allowing compressed air to flow to the brake cylinder and build up a pressure in the chamber C. This pressure reacts downwards on the piston 14, and tends to balance the force exerted through the diaphragm. As soon as a pressure has been reached in the brake cylinder proportional to the degree to which the vacuum brake has been applied, the balancing piston 14 will be forced downwards and the inlet valve 26 will seat. This will take place recurrently as a graduated application is being made.

Supplementary Release Control Valve for Air-Brake.

The object of the valve (Fig. 36) is to secure a graduated release and control the escape of air from the brake cylinders, so that effective

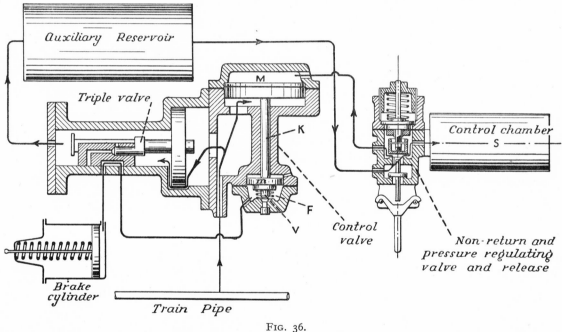

FIG. 36.

pressure can be maintained over considerable periods—a very desirable feature when operating trains on steep and long inclines.

The body of the valve contains two piston-diaphragms (M) and (*m*), the larger one being subject to the full pressure on its upper face, maintained in the control chamber (S) through the non-return valve and on its lower face, the pressure of air in the train-pipe. Between (M) and (*m*), a spindle (K) passes air-tight through the valve casing.

Piston-diaphragm (m) has attached to it the valve (V) controlling the exit of air from the brake-cylinder to the atmosphere; a spring (F) assists in holding this open during normal working.

The action of the valve can be followed from the drawing, which shows the device in "running" position with air feeding past the different ports and connections from the main train-pipe. On making an application of the brakes by reduction of the pressure in the train-pipe, piston-diaphragm (M) is pressed down by the superior pressure maintained above it, by air stored in the control chamber (S), and similarly piston-diaphragm (m) is depressed by the spindle connecting the two, and valve (V) is closed against the resistance of spring (F). On release being required, high-pressure air entering from the train-pipe lifts piston-diaphragm (M), relieves (m), and the valve (V) is opened by action of the spring; as soon, however, as the air pressure in the brake-cylinder is reduced sufficiently to enable the pressure on the upper side of piston-diaphragm (M) to overcome that existing below it (of the train-pipe) plus that of the brake-cylinder and the spring (F), it will be depressed and valve (V) closed, holding the brakes to any desired power. This operation can be repeated as often as required, and the braking power controlled and maintained for indefinite periods; in effect, the brake power becomes inexhaustible as long as air can be supplied from the locomotive.

The second small valve on the control chamber is a pressure regulator, ensuring air being maintained at standard pressure in the control chambers throughout a train. It also forms a non-return and an emergency release valve.

CHAPTER IX

Water Supply—Analysis of Water—Treatment—Feed-water Heating—Weir Pump—Exhaust Steam Injectors—A.C.F.I. Apparatus—Dabeg System—Results obtained from Feed-heating, etc.

Water Supply.

THE water supply for locomotives has undergone much investigation during recent years, as it has been definitely ascertained that to this important factor must be largely attributed the satisfactory life of boilers, fire-boxes, tubes, etc. With the object of preventing corrosion, scale, and pitting, as well as to reduce priming and maintaining healthy steam-raising conditions throughout the period a boiler is in service, some system of treating the feed-water is essential in most districts, and now extensive plants for doing this have been erected at many of the locomotive depot stations on main line railways.

Analysis of Water.

The following analyses are from three important sources of supply on British railways:

Total dissolved solids consisting of—

	A	B	C
	Grains per Gallon.		
Calcium carbonate	33·7	27·2	14·5
„ sulphate	19·6	16·5	3·5
Magnesium sulphate . . .	3·0	5·5	1·3
Sodium chloride	6·6	2·4	4·5
Unimportant constituents . .	0·7	0·5	..
Constituents liable to cause scale .	26·4	22·0	..
Alkalinity	14·5	..	..
Hardness	19°		

This water is subsequently softened by a lime and soda process so as to reduce the hardness to approximately 4 degrees.

The following table is given, taken from a short work on the subject by Sawray and Collett, and is of considerable interest:

Effective Pressure.	Temperature.	
lbs.	Fahr.	
0	212	Carbon dioxide driven off silica, insoluble. Sulphate of lime, less soluble; also carbonate of lime, carbonate of magnesia, less soluble.
20	259	
30	274	
40	287	
50	298	Sulphate of lime, carbonate of lime, carbonate of magnesia, insoluble.

It will thus be seen that up to any temperature likely to be attained by a feed-water heater, the sulphate of lime may be partially removed by blowing off, and by a consideration of these temperatures it may be confirmed that where the feed-water supply is such that undue trouble is not experienced when used in the boiler, there is no adequate reason to hesitate in equipping the locomotives with feed-water heaters on the possible score of excessive cleaning costs and maintenance.

Feed-water impurities have a most injurious effect on boiler efficiency, and are especially undesirable in locomotives, owing to the high evaporative rates at which the latter normally work, the limited and inaccessible places where precipitates accumulate, and often to the varied nature of the available feed-waters. This is so well recognized that railways now find the installation of water-softening plant a well-justified investment; but, even with these precautions, cleaning and washing out at more or less frequent intervals are necessary, since the water treated cold by the usual lime and soda method still retains some hardness. To prevent an excess of alkalinity which would otherwise cause priming and corrosion, the hardness of the crude water is generally reduced to only 4°-5° of hardness, some of which is permanent and forms a hard scale.

Water Treatment.

As an exceptional case of unsuitable water, on one of the South American railways (Nitrate Railways, Chili), this question of water treatment had much study, as considerable trouble was experienced by the excessive priming and damage to the boilers through overheated plates, etc. Further, the cost of repairs was out of all proportion to the reasonable maintenance charges after allowing for the physical difficulties of the country traversed.

Several boiler compounds were tried with negative results, as well as other methods of treating the water, such as lime and soda ash, but as these were found quite unsuitable for the particular conditions appertaining to this railway, " Permutit," base exchange plants of the type shown in Fig. 1 were installed at the following nine stations :

Iquique	100-tons plant.
Molle	50 ,, ,,
Las Carpas	100 ,, ,,
Central	50 ,, ,,
San Antonio	50 ,, ,,
Gallinazos	100 ,, ,,
Pintados	50 ,, ,,
Pozo Almonte	100 ,, ,,
Dolores	100 ,, ,,

An average water hardness of 20° English was taken, and although this, of course, varies at different points, the capacities of all the units were based on this as representing the natural hardness to be encountered.

The most interesting feature of the process adopted is that the water can be softened under pressure, and it therefore only requires to be pumped from a well or other supply, passed straight through the unit under pressure, and then direct to the storage tank, where a constant supply of softened water is maintained. No sludge whatever is formed, the calcium and magnesium salts being entirely removed and converted to their corresponding sodium salts.

After the plant has been running for a certain length of time, the bed of zeolite becomes exhausted and requires regeneration. This is accomplished by using a 10 per cent. solution of brine (sodium chloride), which is passed through the plant by an injector or centrifugal pump, the sodium being taken up by the base-exchange material and the chlorine combining with the calcium and magnesium chloride, which leaves the plant as a clear effluent.

Following this operation, all traces of salt are washed from the bed, and after a certain number of gallons have passed through, a soap test is made, and as soon as " lather " is shown with a specified number of drops of soap solution, this is a signal that completely soft water is again available for service.

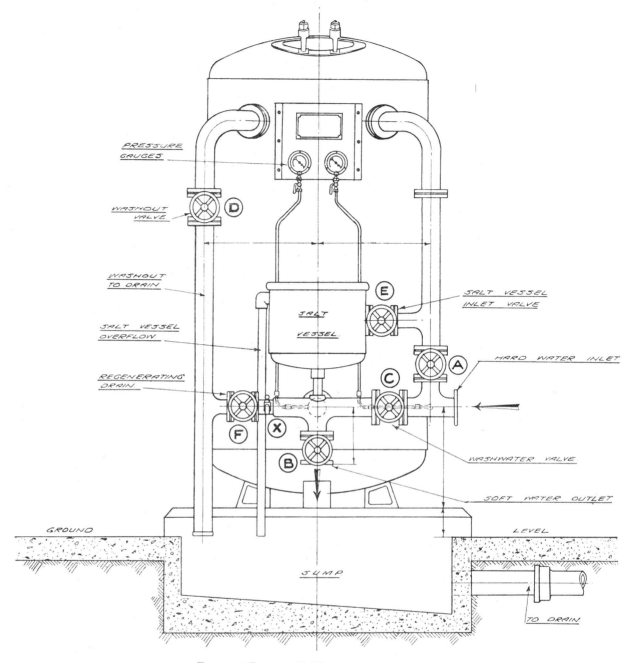

FIG. 1.—"PERMUTIT" WATER-SOFTENING PLANT.

A. Hard-water Inlet Valve.
B. Soft-water Outlet Valve.
C. Wash-water Valve.
D. Washout-valve.

E. Salt Vessel Inlet Valve.
F. Regenerating Drain Valve.
X. Test Tap.

Two or three average analyses of the waters that are being treated are as follows:

Four samples of water received from Tarapaca:

	Grains per Gallon.			
	"A"	"B"	"C"	"D"
Total residue left on evaporation on drying at 230 ft.	42·50	43·54	43·40	42·14
Lime	5·25	5·37	5·41	5·37
Magnesia	·68	·71	·71	·71
Alumina and iron oxide	·21	·21	·21	·21
Chlorine in chlorides	4·80	5·00	4·80	4·90
Sulphuric acids (anhydride)	11·40	12·01	12·24	11·88
Nitric acid (anhydride)	·21	·28	·21	·28
Soluble silica	5·39	5·32	5·32	5·04
Nitrogen in nitrates	·05	·07	·05	·07
Free ammonia	·001	·001	·001	·001
Albuminoid ammonia	·002	·002	·001	·001
Oxygen absorbed by oxidizable organic matter, etc., from a solution of permanganate of potash at a temperature of 80 F.—				
In 15 minutes	·005	·008	·008	·013
In 4 hours	·013	·013	·016	·031
	Deg.	Deg.	Deg.	Deg.
Total hardness	11	11½	11½	11
Hardness after boiling	8	8	8	7

Two samples of water received from Dolores and Lagunas:

	Dolores.	Lagunas.
	Grains per Gallon.	
Total residue left on evaporation on drying at 230 ft.	92·96	60·34
Lime	5·49	2·59
Magnesia	1·00	·76
Alumina and iron oxide	·28	·21
Chlorine in chlorides	30·30	15·50
Sulphuric acids (anhydride)	16·51	10·80
Nitric acid (anhydride)	1·92	0·26
Soluble silica	4·90	4·83
Nitrogen in nitrates	·50	·07
Free ammonia	·001	·001
Albuminoid ammonia	·001	·001

	Dolores.	Lagunas.
	Grains per Gallon.	
Oxygen absorbed by oxidizable organic matter, etc., from a solution of permanganate of potash at a temperature of 80° F.—		
In 15 minutes	·015	·012
In 4 hours	·022	·030
	Deg.	Deg.
Total hardness	12·3	6·5
Hardness after boiling	8·0	2·0

The savings that have been effected since the installation of these plants have been little short of remarkable, and it is of interest to record that in three months after the water treatment had been installed the fuel consumption had dropped on the heavy sections of the line by 30 per cent. Similar savings were effected in water consumption, due to the prevention of leakages and also the elimination of scale, resulting in better utilization of the fuel.

Due to improved boiler conditions the general operation of the railway was improved to such an extent that the number of locomotives required to cover the service was reduced by no less than 25 per cent. With untreated water, the boiler tubes rarely lasted more than 30,000 kilometres, and many fire-boxes had to be changed after less than 100,000 kilometres; some after only 70,000 kilometres. Illustrative of the bad conditions, it is interesting to record that about three years ago 13,000 tubes were changed, spread over only sixty locomotives, which is over 200 tubes per locomotive per annum. After the installation of the water-softening plant all the locomotives which reached 70,000 kilometres had never even had the attention of a boilermaker, and there was one locomotive running on the system which had done over 120,000 kilometres, and the fire-box looked almost as good as it did on the day when it was supplied; there was no sign of scale formation inside the boiler.

This question of treatment has many aspects. It may be, and is often, a fact that the water in certain districts is much better than in others on one railway; furthermore, the traffic, or locomotive mileage, on a section may be so small that it is not a good financial proposition to instal a stationary plant, and to meet this condition a novel arrangement has been introduced in the form of a device applicable to the locomotive itself.

Neckar Apparatus.

Any device of this character that obviates frequent scaling and washing-out operations is likely to prove a valuable accessory, provided, of course, that it is of a simple and reliable type. It is claimed that the " Neckar " system of water conditioning and continuous sludge removal, which has long given excellent results in stationary boilers, and has now in a simplified form been adapted to locomotive engines, admirably fulfils the above conditions and also greatly increases the boiler efficiency, while prolonging the life of the tubes, etc. Moreover, it is said to have the further advantage of keeping the saline or alkaline concentrations at low, fixed limits, thus eliminating priming even at heavy loads; it further provides a safeguard against corrosion.

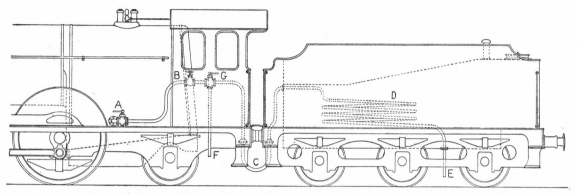

FIG. 2.—ARRANGEMENT OF THE " NECKAR " SYSTEM OF WATER-SOFTENING FOR LOCOMOTIVES.

According to the simplified form of the Neckar system, when the nature of the water involves only " temporary " hardness, it is fed into the boiler in its original state, but where the hardness is partly " permanent," soda ash is added to the feed-tank either in solid form or in solution, and in a quantity proportional to the amount of the water and its permanent hardness. A check on the amount added is acertained by simply testing the boiler water with litmus paper.

During the evaporation the hardness is precipitated in the form of sludge, which, owing to the low concentration, remains in suspension throughout the whole body of water until removed through the continuous sludge-return device which is the cardinal feature of the Neckar system. This, as shown by the accompanying diagram, Fig. 2, consists essentially (though with some variations, according to conditions prevailing on each locomotive) of a pipe line connected to the blow-off cock A on the boiler, which first leads to a regulating cock B in the cab, for adjusting the rate of flow, and thence through a flexible coupling C to a cooling coil D immersed in the tender reservoir; the sludge-laden water being finally discharged through the pipe E. A by-pass F, operated from the three-way cock G, is also fitted.

In this way a small quantity of hot sludge water is continuously removed from the boiler, whereby all accumulation is prevented, the alkalinity and soluble salt concentrations are kept under control and the

FIG. 3.—" TITAN " FEED-WATER HEATER AND PURIFIER.
A. Feed inlet.   B. Removable trays.   C. Outlet for purified water.
D. Central steam passage.   E. Blow-off cock.

sludge is permanently abstracted. The heat in the water is partly restored to the feed-water in passing through a coil prior to discharge. Experience has shown that where a moderately hard feed-water is used a discharge of about 5 to 7 per cent. of the water introduced into the boiler is sufficient to ensure good results.

Feed-water Purifier.

With water which does not particularly require chemical treatment there is still a benefit to be derived from purifying it by causing salts, etc., in suspension to be deposited in suitable apparatus by the heat of the steam in the boiler, so that it can be readily removed. A new device of this description is shown in Fig. 3, as applied to locomotives on the Hungarian State Railways.

The drawing illustrates the construction—the feed-water entering through the pipe A is directed upwards against a deflecting cone, from

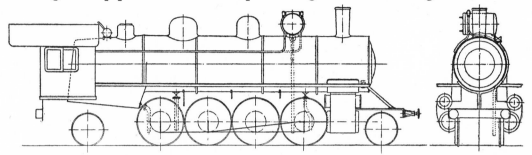

FIG. 4.—2-8-2 LOCOMOTIVE WITH "TITAN" FEED-WATER HEATER AND PURIFIER.

which it falls on to the removable circular trays B. These trays have ribs pressed in them to compel the water to take a spiral course as it falls to the level in the boiler. The cover of the dome is easily removable, and then the trays can be lifted out for cleaning. The water is deflected towards the sides of the boiler, as it leaves the trays, by plates.

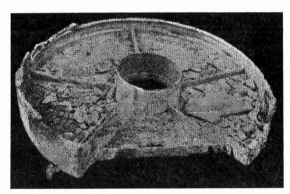

FIG. 5.—A TRAY TAKEN FROM "TITAN" PURIFIER, AFTER 77 DAYS IN SERVICE.

Locomotives fitted with these purifiers operating in districts where the water is notoriously bad can be kept in constant service with "washouts" at monthly intervals—a very important advantage to be obtained from such a simple apparatus.

The illustration (Fig. 5) shows the scale on one of the trays as taken from the purifiers, when these were removed after the locomotive had run some 2,500 miles. The barrel of the boiler had some soft slime, as also the fire-box walls, but this was washed out with the usual water-jet.

The scale on the purifier plates varied from 5 and 6 mm. to 10 mm. thick; in all, 17 kilograms (or 37½ lbs.) was removed from the plates, or dome, of the purifier, and 5 kilograms (or 11 lbs.) from the sides of the dome, or case, and the conduits below.

Feed-water Heating.

To heat feed-water is simple enough, to deliver warm feed is also comparatively easy, but to devise a method of feeding the boiler continuously with water pre-heated to a degree high enough to render the means worth while, has taken years of research and development.

It may be safely said that a locomotive boiler is more highly stressed for output that any other steam generator in commercial use. Subsidiary apparatus is in consequence similarly stressed, and the inference may be drawn that any boiler-feeding device applied to a locomotive must be capable of withstanding the arduous conditions met with in railway operation without demanding an undue amount of extra attention. In this category of subsidiary apparatus must be included feed-water heaters, and these for locomotive use can be divided into the following classes: (1) Surface, or closed types, incorporating in their construction water-tubes deriving heat from either exhaust steam or from flue and smoke-box gases; (2) Direct contact, mixture, or open types, embodying either steam-jet pumps (injectors), steam-driven, direct-acting pumps and jet-condenser chambers, or mechanically driven pumps, comprising jet condensers and surface economizers.

In the case of certain tank engines where it is found convenient to lead a portion of the exhaust steam into the tank and condense it there, a comparatively high rise in temperature of the feed-water is obtained. Fig. 6A on the coloured plate illustrates the general arrangement of the Weir system with pump and exhaust steam heater.

Steam-driven pumps used for feed may be further divided into horizontal and vertical reciprocating, both simple and compound, as well as turbine-driven rotary machines. In the case of mechanical pumps, these are generally operated by a crank-drive from the main engine.

Generally, it may be assumed that if the temperature of the feed-water can be raised by heat, recovered from waste sources, a saving of fuel of 1 per cent. for every 11 degrees rise will be obtained. It will sometimes be found, however, that the actual savings are less than this. On setting out the benefits gained in heat units in tabular form—and including the heat used by the feed-pump—the approximate savings in B.T.U. for an engine with dry, saturated steam at a pressure of 200 lbs. per sq. in. are stated to be 14·4 per cent. in winter and 12·2

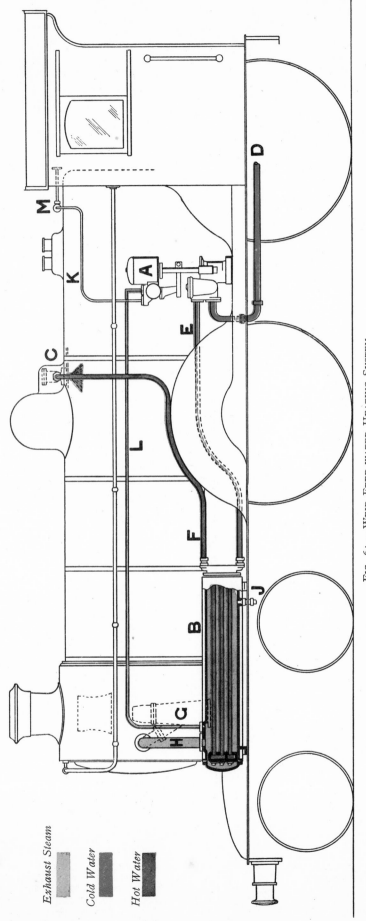

Exhaust Steam

Cold Water

Hot Water

Fig. 6A.—Weir Feed-water Heating System.

A Feed-pump.
B Heater.
C Spray Valve.
D Cold Water Suction-pipe.
E Cold Water Discharge-pipe.
F Discharge-pipe from Heater.

G Blast-pipe.
H Exhaust Steam to Heater.
J Condensate Drain.
K Live Steam to Pump.
L Pump Exhaust.
M Valve for Steam to Pump.

[*To face page* 210

per cent. in summer. For an engine with superheated steam, the figures are given as 13·3 per cent. in winter and 11·3 per cent. in summer.

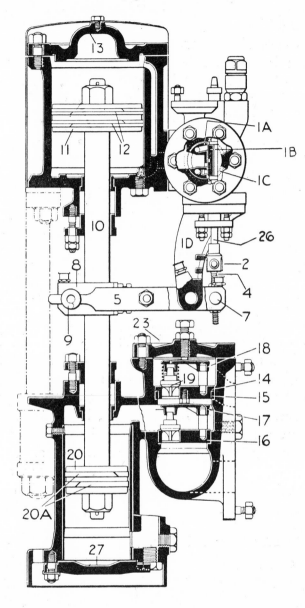

1A. Main slide valve.
1B. Auxiliary slide valve.
1C. Main slide-valve bells.
1D. Bottom cover of piston-valve chest.
1E. Liner for piston-valve chest.
2. Double joint.
4. Bottom spindle.
5. Valve-gear levers.
7. Ball crosshead.
8. Main crosshead.
9. Crosshead pin.
10. Piston rod.
11. Piston body.
12. Piston rings.
13. Cylinder cover.
14. Discharge-valve seat.
15. Discharge - valve - seat ring.
16. Suction-valve seat.
17. Suction-valve guard.
18. Discharge-valve guard.
19. Water valves.
20. Bucket.
20A. Bucket rings.
23. Valve-chest cover.
26. Auxiliary-valve spindle.
27. Pump-bottom cover.

FIG. 6.
WEIR FEED-WATER PUMP.

Well-designed pumps (Fig. 6) have a steam consumption of 2 per cent. of the total evaporation. To effect a comparison with a " live " steam injector, it is necessary to take into consideration the steam used by it. From a thermal point of view, the injector is highly efficient and will deliver, say, 10·7 lbs. of water per lb. of steam at a boiler pressure of 200 lbs. per sq. in. A slight modification is therefore necessary to the figures given, and actual savings for the saturated steam-engine will, probably, be 12·7 per cent. in winter and 10·4 per cent. in summer for the superheated engine, 11·6 per cent. and 9·5 per cent. respectively.

As illustrating the difference between heat saving and fuel saving, results obtained from tests on a 2–10–0 engine, with and without feed-water heater, showed the saving in heat averaged 8·5 per cent., whilst that of coal averaged 15·5 per cent. An increase in the evaporative capacity of the boiler results from feed-heating, a typical example giving a net increase of 12·2 per cent. An increased output from a fitted engine is also to be expected, due to more active evaporation, and hence it is more capable of dealing with severe loads than a similar non-fitted engine.

Usually surface heaters are placed as near the smoke-box as possible, to ensure a short exhaust lead, whilst a feed-pump is fitted either on the same or opposite side of the engine, as may be most convenient. Modifications involve the placing of the heater—generally of cylindrical form—across the smoke-box, forward of the chimney, and either attached by brackets to the shell, or set in a recess in the smoke-box plating, which is shaped to suit.

The surface, or closed type heater, while undoubtedly simple, has the disadvantage of being quickly rendered inoperative when used on engines working in districts having bad water. The high temperature to which the feed is raised causes a proportion of solids to be deposited on the inner surface of the tubes, which becomes not only inefficient as means of transmitting heat, but as passages for the flow of water. There is a further disadvantage in the tendency of leakage and pulling out of the tube-plates. To prevent this, tubes of brass have been adopted of, approximately, $\frac{3}{8}$ in. diameter, and further by providing a special type of valve, by which the direction of the flow can be changed week by week.

Exhaust Steam Injector.

One of the most approved feed-heaters of the first contact, or mixture type, must be mentioned; it is the *exhaust steam injector*, which by reason of its low first cost, light weight, and small bulk commands much favour.

The exhaust injector introduced and perfected by Messrs. Davies & Metcalfe, Ltd., is illustrated in Fig. 7. In practice it is started by merely opening the valve to admit live steam to the injector, and the only other manipulation necessary is the adjustment (when required) of the water regulator, in order to vary the rate of the feed to the boiler.

Its operation is, in fact, even more simple than that of an ordinary live steam injector.

The admission to the injector of exhaust steam, water and auxiliary live steam (used only when the regulator is closed and exhaust steam is not available in consequence) is in each case governed automatically, as also is the overflow valve. The change over from exhaust to live steam working as the engine regulator is closed is also automatic, and practically

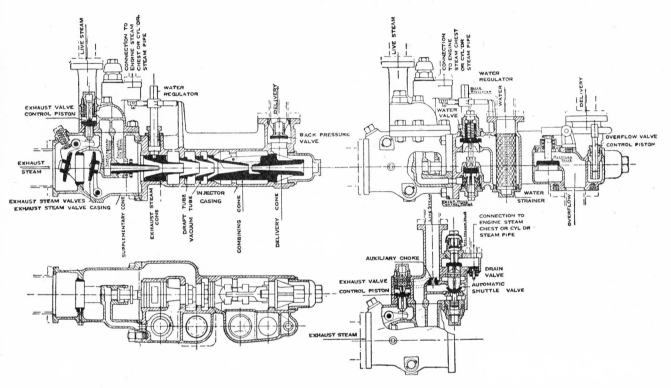

FIG. 7.—DAVIES & METCALFE EXHAUST STEAM INJECTOR.

instantaneous, so that the injector continues to work steadily without waste occurring at the overflow.

Referring to Fig. 7, it will be seen that the exhaust steam is admitted in two separate stages. The first stage comprises a jet of steam admitted through a central cone, the condensing water taking the form of an annular jet surrounding the end of this steam-cone. On meeting the water, the exhaust steam condenses and imparts its momentum to it, with the result that the mixture of steam and water flows forward at a high velocity through the second cone, or " draft-tube," as it is termed. The proportion of steam to water is so arranged that a high vacuum is created within the draft tube, at the end of which the second supply of exhaust steam is admitted in the form of an annular jet. The mixture thereby gains further momentum and, passing through the " vacuum tube," enters the " combining cone," where condensation is completed and the energy available in the steam utilized in its entirety to impart velocity to the water-jet. The latter finally passes through the divergent " delivery cone," thus converting the energy available from kinetic to pressure form, and delivers thence to the boiler.

It will be noticed that the combining cone is constructed on the flap principle, being split longitudinally up to a point near the vacuum tube, where the diameter is such as to facilitate the egress of water and steam. Prompt starting and automatic working of the injector are thus ensured.

Using exhaust steam only, and with feed-water at a temperature of 60° F., the injector is capable of delivering against the following pressures:

Exhaust Steam Pressure. (lbs. per sq. in.)	Delivery Pressure. (lbs. per sq. in.)
1	150
3	165
5	180
10	210
15	240

The delivery temperature ranges normally from 190° to 200° F. with a maximum value of 230° F. The injector reduces the absolute back pressure by about 10 per cent. The exhaust steam consumed represents from 10 per cent. to 12 per cent. of the total, with the result that the smoke-box vacuum is described by 5 per cent.; owing to the increased steam output, however, no change whatever is ever necessary in the draught arrangements. The economy in fuel realized is from 8 to 12 per cent., and that of the water, ranging from 10 to 12 per cent. The injector is capable of adjustment between 50 per cent. and the maximum feed capacity. It will, therefore, be realized that this instrument may be considered as a form of feed-water heater which, in addition to low cost of installation, is both compact and of light weight.

It is now necessary to examine in detail the novel automatic features of the injector. The function of the valve shown by Fig. 8 is threefold. Primarily, it controls the admission of exhaust steam to the injector when the latter is working with the regulator open; it also prevents any return flow of live steam into the exhaust steam-pipe when the injector is working with the former; and lastly, it prevents the entrance of exhaust steam when the injector is not operating.

The outer exhaust valve is of the disc type and is supported by one end of a cranked lever, the other end of which is controlled by a piston. When the injector is not operating, the pressure exerted by the spring shown in the illustration maintains the valve in the closed position and also holds the control piston off its seat. Immediately the injector is started, however, with the regulator open, live steam acts on the top face of the control piston; the latter is forced down on to its seat in consequence, moving the crank lever and opening the outer exhaust valve. Exhaust steam is thus enabled to pass to the inner valve, which is

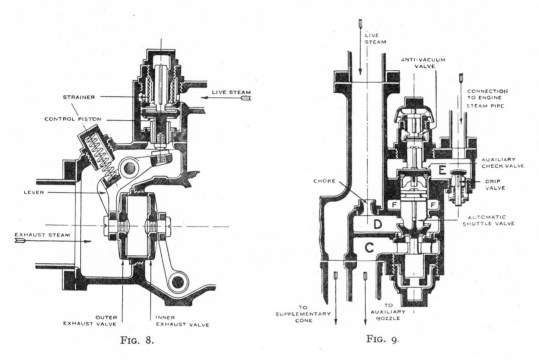

FIG. 8.   FIG. 9.

hinged at the lower side and functions as a non-return valve. Having opened this valve, the exhaust steam then passes into the injector.

When the regulator is closed, the pressure is removed from above the control piston, which rises and allows the outer exhaust valve to close. The auxiliary supply of live steam enters the injector casing and replaces the exhaust steam, at the same time closing the inner valve.

Fig. 9 shows the auxiliary check- and shuttle-valves which effect the automatic change over from exhaust to live steam working, and vice versa. The automatic shuttle-valve comprises a double-seated valve and an operating piston which controls the flow of live steam from chamber D. The function of the auxiliary check-valve is to cut off communication between chamber E and the shuttle-valve piston; it is operated by live steam, taken from the main steam-pipe of the engine and led to E by a suitable connecting pipe.

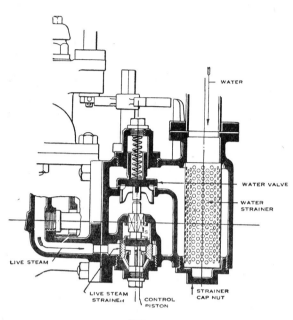

FIG. 10.

With the regulator open, live steam from this source holds the check-valve on its seat, but closure of the regulator causes a fall of pressure in E and the valve is then able to lift under the action of the shuttle-valve. The latter is so arranged that the steam pressure in D, when the injector is at work, will hold it on one or other of its seatings.

Should the auxiliary check-valve offer no resistance, then the shuttle-valve will rise to its upper seating, but will be forced on to its lower seating by the pressure in D if the auxiliary check-valve is held shut.

When the injector is working with the regulator open, the auxiliary check-valve remains shut, the shuttle-valve is on its lower seating, and steam is unable to flow into the injector through passage C. Steam is permitted to flow through passage F to open the exhaust valve, so that the injector works with exhaust steam whilst the regulator is open.

With the regulator shut there is no pressure on the upper side of the auxiliary check-valve. The shuttle-valve therefore rises to its upper seating, admitting live steam to C and, at the same time, cutting off the supply

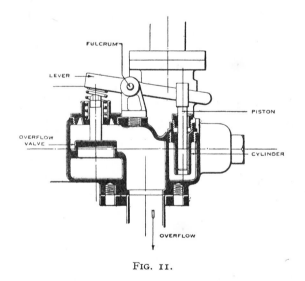

FIG. 11.

of steam to the exhaust valve control piston. The outer exhaust valve consequently closes and the injector works with live steam which, flowing through D, C and the auxiliary nozzle into the injector cones, replaces the exhaust steam.

Ancillary fittings are the anti-vacuum valve, attached to E and preventing chattering of the auxiliary check- and shuttle-valves when the engine is coasting, and a drip-valve.

The water inlet valve is automatically self-closing. It is shown by Fig. 10, from which it will be seen that the feed-water having negotiated the strainer, passes to the upper side of the water-valve. The latter is a drop-valve controlled by a live steam-operated piston, and remains closed until the injector is started.

On opening the steam-valve to work the injector, steam passes to the under side of the control piston and forces it up, thus opening the water-valve and admitting water to the regulator. A seating, S, is provided for the steam-piston and prevents leakage of steam into the feed-water. Closure of the steam-valve removes the pressure from the under-side of the control piston, which drops and allows the water-valve to fall on to its seat, thus shutting off the water supply.

The last automatic valve to which reference is made is that controlling the overflow, and shown by Fig. 11. The overflow valve itself is of the ordinary drop type, and is positively controlled by a small piston located in the delivery chamber of the injector. The piston acts on the valve through a lever which, as shown, has a fulcrum provided for it on the casing. With the injector at work, the delivery pressure on the piston holds the overflow valve to its seat, thus sealing the overflow chamber. Should, however, the injector fly off for any reason, the consequent fall in delivery

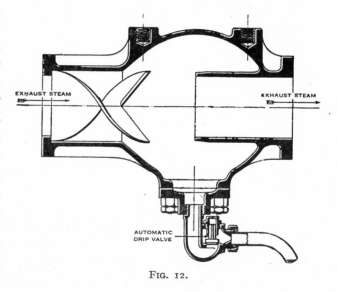

FIG. 12.

pressure causes the overflow valve to open, in which position it remains until normal operating conditions are re-established.

The grease separator, as will be seen from Fig. 12, marks a departure from previous injector practice, and is of the centrifugal type. The helical vane in the inlet passage imparts a whirling motion to the incoming steam, with the result that the heavier particles of grease, dirt or water are thrown off by centrifugal action to the wall of the separator and blown off through the automatic drip-valve at the bottom. The purified stream then passes on to the injector.

The remaining features of the injector do not call for special comment. The admission of feed-water is effected by an eccentrically controlled sliding-cone, and provision is made for a supplementary supply of live steam, to the extent of about $2\frac{1}{2}$ per cent. of the feed, and which is returned, apart from very small losses by radiation, in its entirety to the boiler without thermal loss, to reinforce the exhaust steam when feeding against boiler pressures, which are higher than it can overcome unaided.

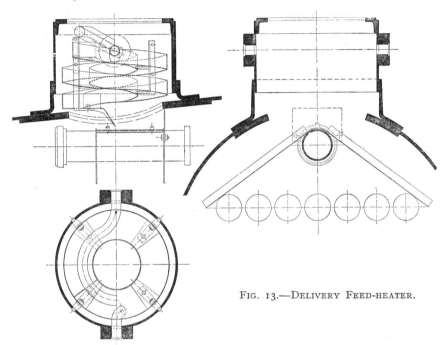

FIG. 13.—DELIVERY FEED-HEATER.

Delivery Feed-heater.

That a saving in fuel can be realized by using heat already in the boiler to heat the feed and therefore increase evaporation per lb. of fuel is, seemingly, at first sight a paradox, but the explanation is that the water temperature of a boiler working at 200 lbs. per sq. in. is 388° F., whilst the normal temperature of the standard injector feed is seldom higher than 160° F. It follows, then, that by using a top-feed injector heater of the type illustrated in Fig. 13, the water entering the steam space is raised to 340° F., or 360° F. Its density is reduced and circulation improved, with a resultant increase in the transmission rate of heat from the tubes to the water.

Further, it should be noted that it is usual to feed the boilers of non-heater fitted locomotives when the engine is stationary, the result being that the comparatively cold feed—by reason of its greater density—falls to the bottom of the boiler, and the temperature, especially in the water-legs of the fire-box, may drop very low. Stresses are then set up, causing leakage at joints, stays and tube ends. It is claimed that such troubles are obviated by using a device of the character described.

A simple and ingenious "heater" is shown in section in Fig. 14. This is mounted on the top of the boiler, so that its nozzle projects as much as possible into the steam space. The delivery pipe from the pump, or injector, is connected to the flange A, and the feed-water passes the back-pressure valve B to the nozzle C of the heater, where it attains sufficient velocity to form powerful induction around the second cone D, drawing in steam, which is immediately condensed, imparting its heat to the incoming

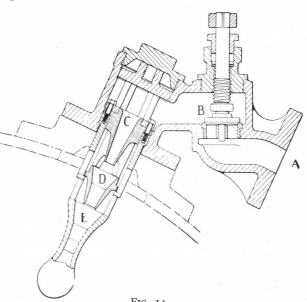

Fig. 14.

water. Similar action is repeated at the final mixing cone E, from which the jet of feed-water is emitted at a temperature claimed to be within 30° F. of the steam. With a steam pressure of 250 lbs. per sq. in. and a temperature of 406° F., the feed-water is delivered at 375° F.

Needless to say, such a means of securing a definitely even temperature of the contents must result in considerable benefits to the boiler, avoiding strains conducive to leaky tubes, stays, etc., with the consequent delays for repair. Improved circulation, there is no doubt, is promoted by the hot feed, and much advantage is derived from the fact that the salts held in suspension are thrown out of suspension with feed-water over 300° F., and when deposited as sludge are readily removable from the boiler barrel at the regular washing-out periods. Gases, too, detrimental to the active heating surfaces of a boiler are driven off before the feed-water actually comes in contact with them.

The device, manufactured by Messrs. Gresham & Craven, Ltd., has now been adopted on a large number of locomotives.

A.C.F.I. Apparatus.

Another successful type of direct contact heater is that known as the
" A.C.F.I.," which is illustrated in the detailed drawing reproduced
(Fig. 15). Exhaust steam is taken from a branch in the blast-pipe,
and, having passed the spring-loaded temperature regulating valve or
thermostat, the function of which is to limit to a predetermined extent
the total quantity of exhaust steam absorbed, enters the mixing-chamber,
together with the exhaust from the feed-water pump itself and the
Westinghouse brake air-pump. All steam utilized for heating the feed
is first freed from any oil which may be in suspension by passing through
a labyrinth of Vee-shaped plates situate in, but partitioned off from, the
mixing-chamber proper. Cold feed-water is pumped into the latter
where, by means of perforations drilled in the top of the induction pipe,
it impinges on the roof of the drum and, falling in the form of a fine
spray, takes up otherwise waste heat from the exhaust steam, at the same
time throwing down impurities which may be present in the feed, and
passes on to the " de-ærating " chamber. The latter is in communication
with the atmosphere, thus accomplishing the liberation of all oxygen
and/or carbon dioxide held in solution in the feed, and operates on the
overflow principle. The feed-water from the mixing-drum enters the
de-ærating chamber by gravity, flows over the lip of the plate defining
the first compartment, into the second, or centre partition, and is
pumped thence through the delivery pipe and clack-valve into the
boiler. Excess of hot feed from the centre compartment overflows the
lip of yet another plate, which is at a somewhat lower level than the first,
and is returned to the hot well.

The horizontal feed-pump has two water cylinders in tandem,
dealing with hot and cold water respectively. That dealing with the
heated water is smaller in size than the cold-water cylinder, thus ensuring
the invariable return of a certain quantity of the feed, heated in excess
of the requirements of the locomotive, to the hot well. The valves
controlling the distribution of steam to the pump are so arranged that
the piston is sensibly decelerated at the commencement and end of each
stroke, thus eliminating the effects of shock, and the pump is in general
designed in such a manner that even when meeting a peak demand the
speed is extremely low, thereby minimizing the maintenance costs of
this important item and at the same time ensuring the abstraction of the
maximum possible number of heat units from the exhaust steam.
Lubrication is effected hydraulically, the lubricator being placed in the
cab; an arm attached to the lubricator cam-shaft gives a visual indication
of each stroke of the pump.

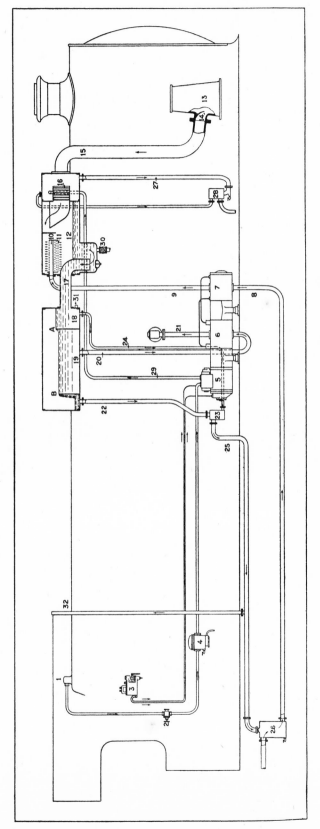

FIG. 15.—A.C.F.I. APPARATUS: SURFACE CONDENSING TYPE.

A. Plate forming intercepting compartment.   B. Plate separating reserve compartment from overflow.
1. Steam stand. 2. Pump stop valve. 3. Lubricator. 4. Steam trap. 5. Pump steam cylinder. 6. Hot water pump. 7. Cold water pump. 8. Suction pipe from tender. 9. Cold water discharge pipe. 10. Perforated spray pipe. 11. Perforated plate. 12. Mixing chamber of heater. 13. Blast pipe. 14. Diverting plate. 15. Exhaust branch to heater. 16. Oil separator. 17. Connecting pipe. 18. Intercepting compartment. 19. Hot water reserve compartment. 20. Feed connection to hot water pump. 21. Hot water delivery pipe to boiler. 22. Overflow pipe. 23. Overflow return valve. 24. Overflow valve equilibrium pipe. 25. Return pipe to suction line. 26. Suction chamber. 27. Oil and water drain pipe. 28. Oil drain and emergency valve. 29. Feed pump exhaust. 30. Heater drain valve. 31. Thermometer boss. 32. Vapour vent pipe.

In normal passenger running on light trains the average feed temperature is 212° to 215° F. On fast heavy, mixed or passenger trains the average temperature rises considerably and remains at about 220° F., often rising to 230° and 240°, the final temperature naturally depending upon the cut-off of the engine. As the mixing of the exhaust steam with the feed-water takes place at a pressure slightly in excess of atmospheric, the feed as delivered may not actually be boiling at these temperatures, but it will, nevertheless, be appreciated that substantial economies in coal consumption will be realized by the equipment of engines with the A.C.F.I. feed-water heating apparatus.

"Dabeg" Economizer.

The drawing, Fig. 16, shows an arrangement of feed-water heating which has been much adopted on the Continent, and has been fitted to some locomotives in this country. The chief novelty is the use of a pump driven direct from the motion of the engine, and so controlled and regulated that it feeds the boiler with hot water in the same proportion as the demand for steam. It consists of a double force-pump, combined in a massive steel casting with a pre-heater mounted above it; the two forming a compact unit located upon the running-board in any convenient situation. Apart from the piping, the only other essential part of the equipment is the oil-separator, which purifies the exhaust steam before it enters the pre-heater. The plunger seen upon the right-hand side sucks cold water from the tender, and that towards the left forces the heated water into the boiler. Both plungers are co-axial and are horizontal, the drive being effected from a central crosshead connected through a rocking-lever supported by a floating fulcrum and worked by some suitable part of the engine's driving mechanism. In the drawing, the connection is made to the eccentric rod, but in certain other applications the drive is taken from a small auxiliary return crank attached to the trailing coupled wheels; an arrangement which appears to be better, inasmuch as the locomotive valve-gear is spared additional stress.

The dimensions of the plungers are such that the influx from the pump balances the water evaporated when the locomotive is operating at its full capacity; and since the stroke is constant, a device is incorporated for diminishing the amount of feed when conditions are less arduous. This is effected by connecting the reversing arm-shaft with a three-way cock regulator on the cold-water induct; so that as the cut-off is shortened and the steam consumption consequently reduced, a portion of the water drawn in by the cold pump is returned again to the tender-tank, the quantity entering the boiler varying in accordance with the setting of the reversing lever, being least at the smallest admission and greatest at the maximum cut-off. When the engine is coasting, with the reversing lever fully over, the whole volume of water is restored to the source of supply.

After passing the regulator valve, the water is pumped through a

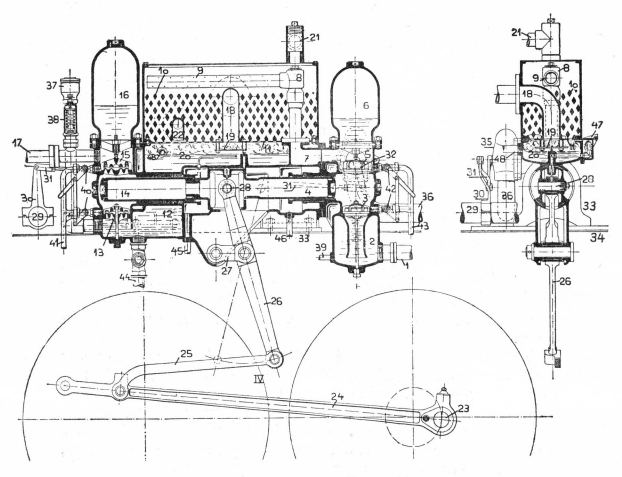

Fig. 16.—"Dabeg" Feed-water Heating Apparatus.

1. Feed-water pipe from water tank. 2. Suction air-chamber of cold-water pump. 3. Cold pump suction valve. 4. Cold-water pump plunger. 5. Cold pump outlet valve. 6. Cold pump air-pressure chamber. 7. Cold-water delivery pipe. 8. Spring-loaded valve. 9. Cold-water spraying pipe. 10. Baffles. 11. Perforated tray. 12. Delivery pump hot well. 13. Delivery pump inlet valve. 14. Delivery pump plunger. 15. Delivery pump outlet valve. 16. Delivery pump air-pressure chamber. 17. Hot-water feed-pipe. 18. Exhaust steam-pipe. 19. Exhaust steam entry. 20. Sump of condenser. 21. Vent pipe to atmosphere. 22. Outlet for uncondensed steam. 23. Return-crankpin. 24. Eccentric rod. 25. Driving rod. 26. Rocking lever. 27. Floating fulcrum link. 28. Plunger cross-head. 29. Reversing shaft. 30. Arm on reversing shaft. 31. Rod connecting arm 30 with 32: Lever of regulating valve. 33. Pedestal supporting body of the apparatus on 34: Running-board. 35. Regulator three-way cock. 36. Cold-water return pipe. 37. Air-pipe for replenishing air-pressure chamber of delivery pump. 38. Spring loaded relief valve. 39. Drain-pipe for cold pump suction chamber. 40. Cocks for 41: Hot pump drain-pipe. 42. Cocks for 43. Cold pump drain-pipe. 44. Sludge-cock. 45 and 46. Drains for water leaking past packing-glands. 47. Lubricator. 48. Connection for overflow pipe.

spring-controlled valve, which renders the incoming stream independent of the pressure prevailing in the condenser, and is finally ejected through a number of small holes that serve to spray the water and cause it to mix intimately with the exhaust steam. The heated water, together with a portion of the condensate, is then forced by the delivery plunger into the boiler through the usual piping and clack-box; the air-chamber above the pump being so proportioned that the pressure does not exceed a predetermined limit. As a further precaution against excess pressure a spring-governed safety-valve is provided in the pressure line. The pump valves are flat, spring-loaded, and of large diameter, thereby avoiding high lift and resulting shock. Drainage of the pump is fully secured by suitable pipes and cocks, so there is no danger of freezing when the engine is out of service in cold weather; and lubrication is effected from a central oil reservoir. The plunger glands and packings are accessibly disposed and fully visible; in fact, all parts of the apparatus have been designed for economical maintenance. A thermometer and pressure gauge are fitted in the hot feed-pipe; and hand control, in addition to that automatically provided, is given by a regulating and shut-off cock placed in the cold intake pipe-line.

As the water is heated to about 212° F. by the exhaust steam, most of the carbonates present in the water are precipitated in the pre-heater, whence they are purged by the sludge-cock at the bottom of the hot-well. This temperature also eliminates gases held in solution, so that the apparatus constitutes a water-feed purifier and de-ærator as well as a heater.

The "Dabeg" apparatus is said to have given very favourable results on the locomotives to which it has been applied, certain tests having shown a fuel economy exceeding 20 per cent. over those fitted with the ordinary injector, and also a decided superiority over steam-driven, hot-water feed-pumps. It is claimed that the mechanical drive is more efficient than the latter, and this may very well be the case; though much will depend upon the accuracy of the relationship subsisting between the quantity of water entering the boiler and the weight of steam evaporated.

Naturally, on engines fitted, an injector is retained as an auxiliary feeder, or for use when the locomotive is stationary. The use of a mechanically driven pump is a reversion to the earliest locomotive practice, but with the refinements embodied in it, the apparatus above described appears to possess many elements of novelty and interest, and its working should furnish valuable information regarding the supply of feed-water to locomotives.